Never Give Up

A Veteran's Journey to Sight and Healing

John C. Malkow
with
Holly Wilson

Published by John C. Malkow
Order information: P.O. Box 740, Murphy, Oregon 97533
Telephone: 541.862.2858

ISBN 0-9741654-0-9

Cover photo by John Raedeke. Photo, page 147 by Douglas N. Naversen, M.D. Used with permission.
Edited by Myrna Daly

Dedication

This book is dedicated to the unnamed thirty-year-old hero who donated his cornea to help an unknown recipient. His selfless gift granted me the miracle of sight and released me from a thirty-year, eleven-month and seven-day prison of darkness.

Forever grateful, John and Family

Contents

Acknowledgment

A special thanks to my daughter and co-author, Holly Wilson, for the many hours of work to transcribe the tapes I recorded to produce this book. I could not have lived my life without the love and support of my family, but this additional labor of love could only be performed by a daughter and can only be repaid with a father's love.

About the Author

John Malkow was a young Army medic when a lab explosion left him blind and disfigured. The blast did not destroy his determination to live his life, or his hope of seeing his two beautiful daughters one day. He struggled with blindness and disfigurement for thirty-one years until he finally heard the words, *I think I can help you.* After a corneal transplant offered the miracle of sight, facial treatments started his path to healing.

Introduction

After a restless night the alarm clock woke us at five o'clock. My wife and I got up to begin the three-hour journey from our home in Murphy, Oregon, to Eugene. Our two daughters, whom I had never seen, joined us in a caravan to the Pacific ClearVision Institute. Heidi, age thirty, and Holly, age twenty-eight, chatted and helped us stay calm as we all faced the day ahead. Anita, my wife of thirty-one years, took the wheel as always as we tried to focus positively on the surgery awaiting me. I wasn't afraid, simply excited to think this would be the last day I would be blind.

At ten o'clock I was escorted into the room where Dr. Scott Cherne, the surgeon who would do the corneal transplant, and Dr. Timothy You, the retina specialist, both examined me. One last check of the measurements, and one last attempt to see through my stained and damaged cornea. After all the medical procedures were finished Dr. You joined Anita and me in a prayer asking God for help and guidance.

As Anita led me back toward the waiting room the staff wished me well, knowing the surgery was a go. During the examination the call had come: the cornea from an unknown donor had arrived at the airport and was being brought to the hospital.

Anita drove me quickly to Saint Anne's Hospital, a few blocks away, where we registered and signed consent forms for the surgery. I was nervous as I was taken to the pre-op area, but I never stopped believing it would be a success. The nurses exchanged my clothes for a hospital gown and had me lie on the gurney that would take me to the operating room. Finally the time had come. I kissed my wife and daughters as the nurse wheeled me away.

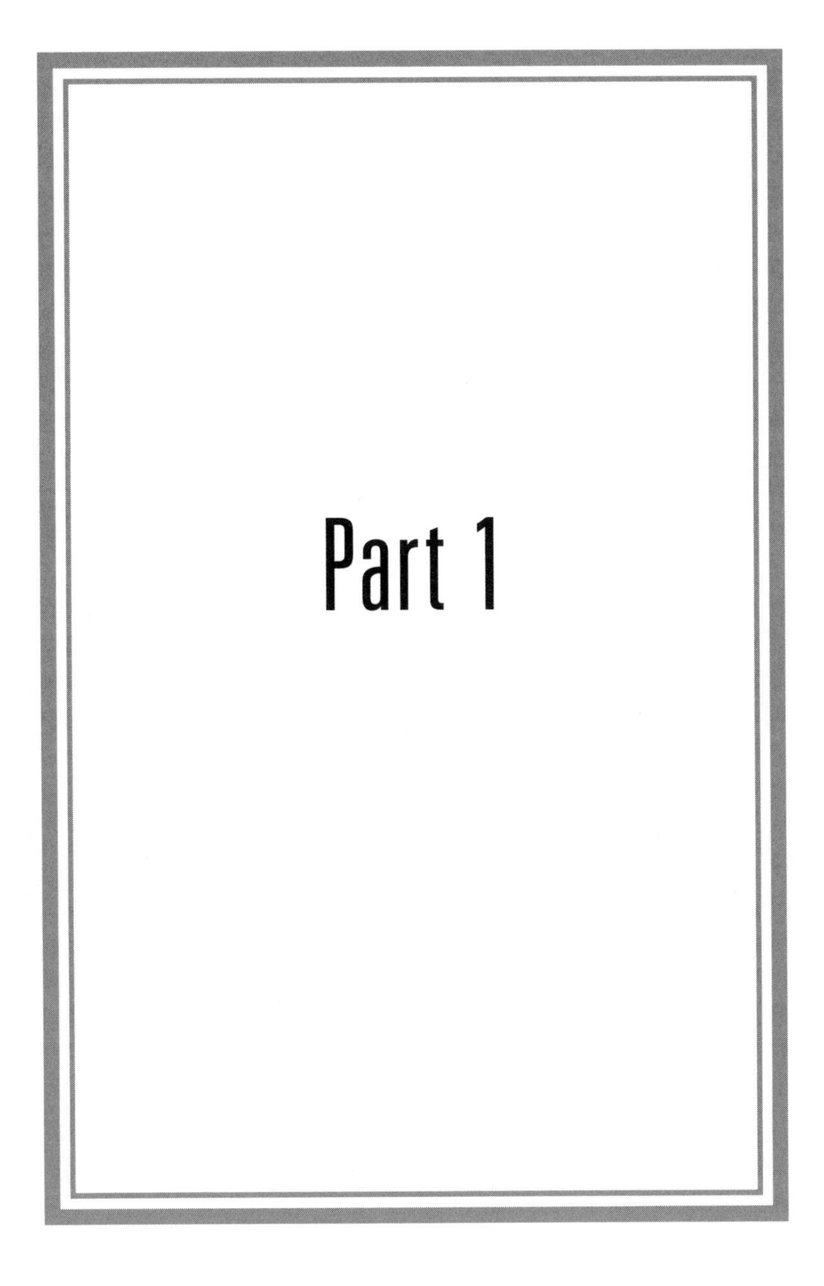

Part 1

Chapter 1

San Antonio and the Army Medical Corps

I was a nineteen-year-old sergeant assigned to B Company, Second Medical Battalion, Second Infantry Division at Camp Irwin, Korea, in 1966 when I realized I wanted to make the U.S. Army my life's work. I also knew that going to school was the best route for career advancement, so with the encouragement of my first sergeant, company commander and battalion commander I applied for Clinical Specialist 91c School. I attached letters of recommendation to my application and submitted them to the Department of the Army, knowing that 91c School took only the best military medics and turned them into the Army's elite Medical Corps.

In July 1967, to my utter disbelief, I learned that I had been accepted to this selective school ahead of a lot of other applicants with higher rank and more time in service. After Company B, I would be assigned to Clinical Specialist 91c School at Fort Sam Houston, Texas.

A month later I took my seat on the Boeing 707 headed back to "the world" — the United States, to military personnel overseas. After landing at McCord Air Force Base outside Seattle I began a slow journey on my thirty-day leave. After spending a few weeks with my father in Modesto, California, in early September I flew to

San Antonio where I cleared post, drew my medical whites and signed in to Clinical Specialist School.

My bunkmate, Sam Maguire, a recent returnee from Vietnam, was also in 91c school. The two of us became friends as we waited for the rest of the class to arrive from Europe, Vietnam, Korea, like myself, and other stations in the U.S. When an opening came up in the non-commissioned officers' billet, Sam and I moved there, teaming up with two other medical corps students, Art Kyalaivas (affectionately known as "Greek") and Bill Affholter. The four of us palled around at night and did our assigned duties during the day.

On October 2 we entered the classroom that would be our home for the next nine months. Promptly at 7:15 A.M., Sergeant Jack Lumburg, the NCO in charge of 91c school personnel, took charge and organized us into two groups that would be divided into teams of four and five when we started our rotations at Brooke Army Hospital. Sgt. Lumburg was to become our teacher, cheerleader, confidant and general morale-booster. It was his job to see that we not only did not fail, but that we succeeded with honors, as we were needed in the Vietnam War. Besides war duty, many of the NCOs would later be assigned to air ambulance helicopters and trained in intensive first aid and lifesaving skills.

Lt. Col. Alice Bender of the Army Nurse Corps was the commanding officer at 91c school, and most of our instructors were Army nurses. Our classroom training covered general administration, medical records and reports, field medical service, anatomy and physiology, dietetics, mental health, surgical and operating room techniques, obstetrics, pediatrics, emergency medical and dental care, managing mass casualties, preventive medicine, medical exams, and general medical care — in all, some 696 hours of classroom instruction.

Later we would be divided into small groups for two- and three-week rotations at Brooke Army Hospital to complete 1,760 hours of training in areas such as general medicine, surgery, field hospital, neurosurgery, recovery room, outpatient service, orthopedics, urinary service, ward administration, obstetrics, newborn care, pediatrics, operating room, central material in service, and a two-week rotation in the surgery research unit at Fort Sam Houston's hospital for intensive burn wounds. Both civilian and military casualties were brought to Brooke Army Hospital, a leading center for surgery and rehabilitation for burn victims.

Our class consisted of forty-five non-commissioned officers, plus fifteen honor graduates from the Army's basic medical training to make up the class of sixty. We all knew the group of eight young women and seven young men had been chosen ahead of others in line for this training, and they were under pressure to excel.

When classes opened we were assigned seats in alphabetical order, and I found myself next to Private Anita K. Johnson. After class the next day — my twentieth birthday — Art, Bill, Sam and I went to the NCO club where one drink led to another and the revelry continued long past bedtime.

The next day I woke up sick, sober and sorry. I was in terrible shape, with the most god-awful headache of my life. I took a cold shower and stumbled to school, hoping to make it through class. But the instructors' words were not sinking in, and I knew I was going to have to do some intensive study that evening to make up for the lost school day. I turned to the young lady next to me and said "Honey would you mind taking some notes for me? I am just awfully sick." She kind of smiled and nodded in response to what were the first words I spoke to my future wife.

As we settled into a routine of going to school each day, eating dinner, studying for an hour or two and then going to the NCO club, my interest in Private Johnson began to increase. She seemed very charming during our conversations between classes, and I finally mustered the courage to ask her out to dinner. We discovered we had a lot in common so we began to go out on dates and study together. Soon the attraction went beyond friendship and grew into true love. As ridiculous as this sounds, after eight weeks we could not do without one another. I loved her, and there was no doubt in my mind that I wanted to spend the rest of my life with her. I was sure she felt the same.

Just before Thanksgiving I asked Anita to marry me. When she said yes I was totally elated. We became even closer, spending every moment with one another. As Christmas approached Anita made plans to go home to Santa Paula, California. She had applied for leave during our two-week class break. Doing the only thing a man should do during the days before his fiancee was to leave, I spent my whole paycheck wining and dining and entertaining her.

The week before Christmas Bill, Art and I drove Anita to the airport. As we kissed good-bye and she boarded the plane for her flight to Los Angles my heart felt empty. I returned to the barracks to face another Christmas basically alone. I had been in Korea the previous year and spent Christmas with other soldiers from my unit of Company B second medical battalion. Sitting in the barracks, with nearly everyone gone for Christmas, I suddenly got a flash. I looked in my wallet — it was as empty as the barracks around me. I looked at the Seiko wristwatch I'd bought in Korea and thought to myself, This could be your way out. I asked Bill to drive me off-post, where there was a row of pawnshops immediately outside the gate. I walked into a pawnshop, took my watch off and laid it on the front counter.

"How much is this worth?" I asked. After examining it closely the pawnbroker said he would allow me eight dollars on it. That's better than nothing, I thought. So I pawned my Seiko watch for eight dollars and went back to the barracks to pack my things.

"I'm going to hitchhike to Santa Paula and spend Christmas with Anita," I said to Bill.

"You certainly have to be out of your mind," he said. "It's wintertime, it's cold — and it's snowing. How do you think you're going to make it hitchhiking?"

"I don't know," I said, "but where there's a will there's a way."

Bill drove me to a truck stop in a little town called Hondo, just outside San Antonio. It was cold, windy and spitting snow, so I went inside to get a cup of coffee and warm up. Immediately a truck driver walked up and said, "Where are you headed, son?"

"I'm going home for Christmas," I replied. "I'm heading to Los Angeles."

"I'm going to Phoenix," he said. "Why don't you jump in and I'll give you a ride."

At the truck stop where he turned off the driver simply walked inside and announced, "This young man is going home for Christmas. Anyone headed towards L.A.?"

Another trucker immediately offered a ride all the way to Barstow, California, buying dinner and breakfast along the way. He wouldn't allow me to spend a penny of my eight dollars.

Before turning south at Barstow the driver pulled into another truck stop and asked if anyone was going to L.A. Two drivers were headed that way and told me to throw my stuff in the back and get in. I was on my way.

Along the freeway I saw a sign for the Richfield Building, and from trips through Los Angeles as a child I remembered that the Richfield Building wasn't far from the Greyhound Bus Station, so I asked the driver to pull over and let me off.

"Are you crazy? It's five o'clock in the morning."

"No I'm not crazy," I said. "I have to get to the bus station and figure out how to get to Santa Paula." I jumped out of the truck, grabbed my stuff and waved good-bye to the drivers. They were right — there was no one on the streets at that hour, but I just kept walking towards the blinking Richfield sign in the distance.

A policeman gave me directions, and I walked into the bus station around seven. I ordered a cup of coffee while I warmed up and figured out what to do next. I called information and got Anita's telephone number. She answered and asked where I was.

"I'm in Los Angeles," I said. "How do I get to Santa Paula?"

"You are *where?"*

"I'm in Los Angeles. Where's Santa Paula?"

"How in the world did you get to Los Angeles?"

"I hitchhiked."

"How in the heck did you do that?"

"I don't know," I said, "but I beat the bus. I got in with some truckers and they brought me here on a nonstop trip."

She told me Santa Paula is north of Los Angeles so I went to the counter and bought a ticket for a little over two dollars, and Anita and her mother were there to meet me when I arrived about noon. I was an awful sight after two days in a semi truck. After cleaning up and trying to make myself presentable Anita and I talked.

"Say," I began, "as long as I'm here and everyone else is here, including your mom, why don't we get married?"

"Well, that's just fine," she said.

Her mother had thrown her a wedding shower the night before. Anita received all kinds of wedding gifts, things we would use over the next thirty years. Anita's mother, as I would come to learn, was always in for a good time. She thought a wedding was a splendid idea and promptly called Anita's Aunt Gladys in Santa Barbara. The four of us left for Las Vegas on the morning of December 24, 1967. After lunch we walked around town awhile, then decided it was time.

We bought a wedding license, which Anita had to pay for because I had no money. To this day I don't see what Anita's parents saw in me, but they somehow knew I was the right guy for their daughter. Anita and I said our wedding vows at a small chapel called Wee Kirk of the Heather at three o'clock in the afternoon of December 24, 1967. The people in Las Vegas were splendid to us — two kids, just getting married. There was hardly anyone in town. Las Vegas was a lot smaller then, basically just downtown and a few casinos out on the strip.

December 24, 1967. Anita and I were two kids, full of love and hope for the future.

We stayed downtown at the Mint Hotel. Everywhere we went people would ask us what we were doing there. When we answered that we had just gotten married they'd say "Let us buy you dinner" or a drink.

After three days it was time to return to Santa Paula and the realization of what I'd done hit home. How would I get back to San Antonio? Knowing that I could get transportation back to base, I went to Fort McArthur and asked for a convenience ticket to fly back to San Antonio. The cost would be taken out of my pay over a six-month period.

It was my job to go home, collect my pay, find a place to live, buy a car — all the things we needed to start our life together. All the guys were back from leave then, and everyone went on a search for a car we could afford, about $100 to $150. I found an apartment a couple blocks from base, one of those low-rent places that surround most military bases. We bought a 1957 Chevrolet with a six-cylinder engine — a real piece of junk, but it was the nicest thing we had.

Anita arrived in San Antonio two days later with all her wedding presents. We had enough blankets, towels and everything, except silverware. At the grocery store I spotted a set of silverware for four for $4.95. I still have that silverware today in my trailer.

Anita and I reported back to school the first week of January and shared the news of our wedding. As we began making decisions about our careers and our future we soon discovered that we would not be guaranteed assignments together or anywhere near each other. The Army simply didn't do that in those days. Our only recourse was for Anita to become pregnant to be released honorably from the Army. We'd not only had a whirlwind romance, now we had to start a family.

In less than three months we had made all these decisions, certain that we would be together forever. Being dutiful newlyweds this next step was achieved quickly. Soon Anita had morning sickness and we realized our dream had come true. Anita and I continued to attend school and fulfill our military duties. In March, after Anita was examined by a military doctor and found to be pregnant, she was discharged from Army.

Our class had begun the clinical portion of the school, and Art Kyalaivas and I drew our first assignment together. We were to spend two weeks in the communicable disease department, taking care of patients with spinal meningitis, pneumonia and other diseases to learn nursing care of the highest level.

Time passed quickly. Every two weeks we went to a different part of the hospital. In April, after one week in the pediatric ward I had an upper respiratory infection and came down with diarrhea and severe stomach cramps, probably from a virus the children on the ward had. It seemed everyone who rotated into pediatrics came down with something.

I went to the orderly room at the school to tell Sgt. Lumburg that I was too sick to go to work. As I signed into sick call he said he hadn't been feeling well either and decided to join me. We went over to the dispensary together, where I was treated and sent home. Sgt. Lumburg saw the doctor and was admitted to the hospital, where his diagnosis was lymphosarcoma — cancer of the lymph nodes — which was terminal at that time. Sgt. Lumburg died three days before we graduated and was buried on our graduation day. Everyone felt the loss of this wonderful man and mentor.

Fifty-one students of the original sixty graduated. Nine didn't make it — Anita and another woman had married and become pregnant and left the service. Some of the others simply could not make the grade. My friend Sam Maguire was dismissed from school; he had volunteered for his next assignment back in Vietnam. Sometime in June 1968 Sam Maguire became one of the 53,000 casualties in the Vietnam War. Sam was killed in action in Southeast Asia as part of the United States Army's war machine.

Graduation day for some of us was bittersweet. Success was achieved, our studies were finished and we were now 91c and waiting for our assignments. The loss of Sgt. Lumburg, however, was a shadow over the celebrations. Farewell parties were mostly subdued as we took off for different parts of the world.

Some guys went to Vietnam for the first time, some went to Europe and the Hawaiian Islands, and others stayed in the United States. My assignment, because I had been in Korea for thirteen months before attending school, was Madigan General Hospital in Seattle, Washington.

In the late afternoon of July 19, 1968, with diploma in hand and baggage packed in the car, my wife Anita and I made our way to Santa Paula, California, on our way to my first assignment.

Chapter 2

Life Changes in a Flash

After spending two weeks with Anita's folks in southern California we drove north on Interstate 5, stopping in Grants Pass, Oregon, to visit my grandparents and introduce Anita to my family. When we reached Fort Lewis, Washington, I cleared post but with no assignment waiting, Anita and I had time to explore the area. We visited Anita's aunt and uncle, who had a cabin on the beach at Vashon Island. In August and September the Pacific Northwest is one of the most beautiful spots in the world. From their cabin we could see the waterfront of Tacoma, around to Des Moines and all the way to Seattle. On those clear, sunny days it seemed as if we could reach out and touch Mount Rainier.

The days sped by. After checking in at the post each day I was free to take my wife by the hand and go for long, leisurely walks on the beach hunting for shells and enjoying the scenery. After six days I learned that I was to be posted to the U.S. Army dispensary at Fort Lawton, another lovely spot north of Seattle on Puget Sound. I was to provide nursing care and supervision at the dispensary and to hold sick call at a Nike missile site on one of the small islands in Puget Sound.

Anita was in the third trimester of her pregnancy when we settled into our quarters at Fort Lawton. I began my daily routine of going to work at 7 A.M. and reviewing procedures with the staff from the office, pharmacy, x-ray department and medical lab.

My routine included ferry rides out to the islands for sick call and stops in the dispensaries to see if the staff needed help. On one of these visits, at 10 A.M. on the morning of September 17, 1968, I walked into the medical laboratory to ask Specialist Wilson if I could do anything to help him. This visit was to be the beginning of a thirty-year, eleven-month and seven-day nightmare.

The day had started out misty and overcast, foretelling the end of summer and the beginning of fall. As the morning went on I glanced out the window as I made my way to x-ray, the farthest point in the dispensary, then to the medical supply room and finally the laboratory. I opened the door but found no one at the front desk. When I called for Specialist Wilson he answered from the back of the laboratory. I walked down the hall and found him wearing a lab coat, mixing something in a porcelain mortar. As we chatted about his daily assignment the buzzer rang, indicating that someone was in the front office. As he left I asked if there was anything I could do.

"Would you mind stirring the mixture in the bowl?" he asked.

"Sure," I said. The bowl was sitting on a laboratory table. The table had about a four-inch maple surface with a suspended shelf running down the center about twenty inches above the tabletop. There were beakers, bowls, petri dishes and various kinds of medical and laboratory equipment on the table and shelf and in the surrounding cupboards.

I reached up and took a wooden tongue depressor from the box on the shelf above. Suddenly, just as it touched the mixture I saw a beautiful bright light that seemed to be at the end of a pipe, much like looking with a flashlight through a culvert at night. The small light broadened into a warm yellow glow, and my ears began to ring. I realized something had gone wrong. I had been slammed against a wall, I was short of breath and I felt an intense pain across my face, hands, chest and abdomen.

I can remember holding up my hands against the light. Immediately I knew my right thumb was gone. My other fingers were badly broken, twisted and misshapen. My thumb dangled from my left hand, but those fingers were functional. I laid them against my chest and began to scream for help. By the time I got to the hall and laid down on the floor Specialist Wilson was by my side, and within two or three minutes he had two doctors there. I was given first aid and painkillers for the intense pain and an IV line, as I was bleeding profusely from the puncture wounds. The force of the explosion drove pieces of wood from the table and tongue depressor, porcelain from the bowl, and the chemicals themselves into my skin, muscle and bone.

The pain began to subside and I was coherent enough to talk to the doctor and others around me. I thought of my wife, Anita, eight months pregnant with our first child, and I asked Dr. Roe to please not let anyone from the dispensary tell my wife what had happened. He assured me that, as soon as I was taken to the hospital, he would take charge of Anita. Just then the ambulance from our dispensary arrived to rush me to Public Health Hospital in downtown Seattle, the hospital responsible for major injuries to medical personnel and their dependents. Dr. Roe rode with me for the thirty-minute ambulance trip, then turned me over to the eight or nine doctors on the scene and went to attend to my pregnant wife. The staff of general and thoracic surgeons examined me for abdominal injuries. I had severe pain in my right rib area, which I later learned was from the drawer knob on the laboratory table exploding against my abdomen. It caused severe bruising but no puncture wound. My face was on fire, and my hands were in agony.

The doctors found no major puncture wounds, chest wounds, or life-threatening injuries other than loss of blood. Next an orthopedic surgeon examined my hands and called for x-rays. Dr. Donald R. Wright, an ophthalmologist assigned to the U.S. Coast Guard, was in attendance to examine my eyes. He asked me to open my eyes. He first shined a light into my right eye and asked if I could see it. In several positions I could see the light, and in other positions I couldn't. When he repeated the procedure in my left eye I could see top, front, left, right, and nothing else.

Next I was sent for x-rays of my face and hands, which had received the worst injuries. The pain was excruciating, and the x-rays took longer than I had hoped. The positions I had to put my mangled hands into for the x-rays needed for reconstructive surgery were nearly unbearable. Finally they were finished and I was wheeled into the operating room. Dr. Wright was there, holding my arm and telling me to rest assured that I was in good hands. All I could think was, Please put me to sleep so I can end this pain. Finally the sodium pentothal flowed through the IV and I was gone into a long, dark sleep that lasted eight hours.

When I awoke after surgery I found myself sitting in a reclined position with my eyes bandaged and both hands in casts hung on IV poles above my head. My wife Anita was at my side. What a blessing and a source of strength. I asked if she felt like she was going into labor but she assured me she was doing fine and trying to stay calm. We were both worried about our child.

For the next five or six days I would awaken to find Anita by my side. Then I would drift off again into a long sleep from the pain medication. Gradually the narcotics were reduced so that I could maintain some bodily function, and I began to stay awake for longer periods of time.

Finally I was well enough to sit up for short periods in a wheelchair and be wheeled to the eye clinic where Dr. Wright examined his handiwork.

Our conversation began as he unwrapped the bandages. I don't know how hard it is to tell someone they might be blind for the rest of their life. Dr. Wright started by saying "John, your right eye was totally destroyed and I had to remove it."

"That's OK," I told him. "I still have my other eye." Looking back, I can't believe I cut him off and didn't give him a chance to explain the injuries. When you're twenty years old you think you're invincible. I thought my eyes were just full of dirt and debris, never dreaming that I would be blind.

Looking into my left eye Dr. Wright said things were progressing, that there was a traumatic cataract forming to protect the retina. Later this could be removed and possibly my eyesight could be restored. Trying to take this in stride and remain positive, I simply said that when the time comes I'll have the operation and I'll be able to see.

After ten days in the intensive care unit I was moved onto the ward. Dr. Wright saw me daily, spending many hours examining me, trying to make sure everything was healing until we could come up with the treatment to save my eyesight. It would be another four to six weeks before the orthopedic doctors would know the results of their work on my hands.

On October 4, 1968, I spent my twenty-first birthday with my eyes bandaged and my hands above my head. Anita came in as always about 9:30 A.M. She had to leave in a few hours, she said, but promised to come back to feed me dinner.

At five o'clock Anita returned with a surprise. After dinner all the guys I had worked with at the dispensary came, and Anita brought out a birthday cake she had made that afternoon. While celebrating my birthday I learned what the explosion had done to the lab. The force of the blast blew out sixty-seven windows, broke every bottle and piece of glass in the lab and blew a porcelain bowl down through the four-inch-thick maple lab table. The upward blast blew a three-foot hole through the ceiling and roof. I was extremely lucky to be alive, having caught only the side draft of the explosion. I was told the chemicals had been in storage and were very old and unstable.

Anita spent most of her time by my side taking care of me, giving me food and water. She was the strongest individual I have ever known in my life, and her care has never ceased for more than thirty years.

On October 9 I was released from the hospital and Anita and I went to our home in Fort Lawton. When we arrived home Anita and I took a long rest, just being together. The next afternoon our daughter Heidi Lynn Malkow decided to begin making her way into the world. When Anita went into labor we immediately called our friends Mel and Judy Dykstra, who also lived on base. We all loaded into the car and headed for Swedish Hospital in downtown Seattle. Anita was admitted to the hospital and the next morning at 10:08 A.M. Heidi was born. It was the most wonderful feeling — the birth of my first child.

For the next three days I stayed with my father and his new wife in Seattle, where he had taken a job at Boeing Aircraft

Company. When Anita was released from the hospital and we returned home, she not only had a new baby but also a blind husband. Her mother came from Santa Paula as soon as I called to tell her Heidi was born. Madge was there to help with the care of the baby so Anita could continue to take care of me. This was a big job. I had been sleeping so much I had days and nights mixed up and so did the baby. There was always somebody eating or sleeping at all hours. It was difficult for me to tell night from day because to me it was dark all the time, but finally I got on a schedule. Soon it was time for Madge to go home. She had a business to run and had literally shut it down to take care of us. This example of parenthood would stay with me for a lifetime with my children.

I was being checked by the doctors at Madigan General Hospital outside Tacoma, rather than by Dr. Wright. Days stretched into weeks and months, then word came that I was to be sent to Fitzsimmons General Hospital in Denver, the eye center for the U.S. military. Each Army hospital had a specialty. Walter Reed was for intestinal and heart, Brooke at Fort Sam Houston was for burns, Madigan was orthopedics and Fitzsimmons was for eyes and amputees.

After we spent Christmas with her family Anita took me to McCord Air Force Base in Tacoma where an air ambulance would take me to Fitzsimmons General Hospital. Anita was to go home, pack her things and fly to California to spend the next year with her mother.

When we reached the airfield near Denver there were buses set up like ambulances for the guys who were unable to walk. A nurse escorted me from the plane to the bus bound for Fitzsimmons Hospital.

Once admitted I was taken to 4 West, the ladies ward — what a place to put a blind guy! Later that afternoon a staff of doctors examined me, looked at my eye, asked a lot of questions and reviewed my records. They told me I would be seen the next day, so I was taken back to my room to wait and wonder what my treatment would be. I was sure I would be seeing in nothing flat. I would have the recommended treatment and return to my job.

The next morning I was examined and assigned a doctor, Major Carney. During the exam he told me the cataract in my eye wasn't ready for surgery, but he assured me it would be only a short time until the procedure would be done and he was hopeful that it would be successful in restoring some of my eyesight.

I saw Dr. Carney every day or two for the next few weeks. Each time he would say the eye was not quite ready yet.

After I spent the first week alone in a double room, a young man was brought in from Vietnam. Dennis Walker was twenty-two years old and had been injured and blinded by an explosion from a booby-trap bomb. Like me, he had lost an eye and couldn't see out of the other. Dennis was hopeful his eyesight would be restored at the same time as mine. The two of us began a long, intense friendship that lasts to this day.

Finally in the third week of January my cataract was ready and so was I. I could take off this mask of blindness and move forward with my life.

At seven the next morning I was wheeled to the operating room. Dr. Carney came in and explained that he was going to put a knife in my eye and slice the front of the cataract, wash out the debris from the inside of my lens, suction out the remainder and restitch my eye, then replace the fluid in the front of my eye. I was almost jubilant, I was so eager for this operation. Dr. Carney scrubbed up, then came over and scrubbed my face and began the procedure. He gave me a shot to relax me and then placed his finger under my left eye, pushing down to move my eye out of the way. Then he plunged a needle under my eye to the back. I had never had anything hurt so much; the pain was unbelievable. Dr. Carney kept repeating "Don't move your eye, don't move your eye," as he injected the numbing medicine.

In a few seconds there was no more pain and he began to work. I could see a very fine wire moving around inside my eye, then a fluid would wash things away. Things seemed lighter — nothing was clear but I knew it was going well. I felt positive, for the first time in months.

After the surgery I was taken back to my room and moved into bed with sandbags on both sides of my head. I was not to move.

I could not get out of bed at all, even to go to the bathroom. I had to lie flat on my back, and if I wanted anything I had to call the nurse. I couldn't lift my head to eat, drink water, or anything else. I had to lie still for three or four days. Dr. Carney would come in frequently, remove the bandage and shine a light in my eye to check my vision. I could see a light; it was dim but I could see the light. I assumed this was normal.

Finally after five days I was taken to Dr. Carney's office. I was placed behind a large magnifying glass with a light called a slit lamp where I spent hours and hours as Dr. Carney tried to remove the debris from my cornea. On my first post-operative visit he told me that he removed the cataract as well as two pieces of wood from my eye. He was amazed, and asked several questions about the accident and where the wood came from. I told him it had to be the tongue depressor I had had in my hand.

Every two or three days for the next two weeks I would be wheeled to the eye clinic so Dr. Carney could check my eye. I could see light but not too much else, and I was beginning to get concerned. I thought things should have progressed further by this time. Dr. Carney assured me that we might have other options, but he explained that there was a problem with my interoculate pressure. It's at zero, he said, and it doesn't seem to want to come up. We really don't know what the problem is, he told me, but we will continue to keep an eye on you. This didn't sound good. The idea that I would have cataract surgery and be able to see again was beginning to look doubtful.

Time seemed to crawl by as I waited for my eye to improve. Next it was Dennis's turn. His cataract was ready for the same procedure that I had had. When he came back to the room Dennis said when they took the cataract off he could see things moving around. Things were blurry, he said, but he could see his face and the doctor's hands moving. This is not looking good, I thought to myself. I hadn't seen anything like that.

Dennis's eyesight began to improve, and after a week or so he could see well enough to walk without a cane. He used to take me places. "Hang on," he'd warn, and off we'd go. We finally had an escape from that room, which seemed more like an incarceration than a hospitalization. It was a pleasant break just to go sit in the hall, open a window and smell the fresh air.

It was obvious that I was not improving, so Dr. Carney thought I might do better with a rest at home. I was given a thirty-day convalescent leave to be home with Anita and our baby.

Anita met me at the Los Angeles airport and drove me to Santa Paula to her parents' house. We would lie out in the sun and talk for hours. Anita would lead me places, as I couldn't go anywhere without holding on to someone's arm. My baby was growing. She was the cutest little thing you ever saw. I couldn't see her, but I knew she had to be.

Heidi was born two weeks after the explosion that left me blind. The facial discoloration hadn't started yet, but the blindness meant I would wait over thirty years to see my daughters.

All too soon the thirty days were up, and Anita took me to the airport for the flight back to Denver. The day after I returned to Fitzsimmons Hospital I was called back to the eye clinic for another exam. I was there for hours and there was no change. I could only see the light. I could see a hand waving in front of the light but nothing else. Dr. Carney started to remove debris from my cornea again. He would put my eye to sleep and use a needle in my eye to remove the debris, hoping this might open up a small window through which I would be able to see. My eye pressure wasn't coming up; it was still at zero.

It had been almost two months since the operation. I knew things were not progressing, and I asked Dr. Carney if there was anything else we could do. He said maybe if your eye pressure comes up we can do an operation called a vale, a procedure that takes the sac the cataract was in and splits it open so that it works like a curtain. Maybe that will help in locating more debris that we can remove, he suggested. Maybe things will clear up then. But it was not yet a possibility. We would have to wait until my eye pressure increased.

I went back to my room and began to sit and wait, and wait, just waiting for something to happen. I would be seen every two or three days, then once a week. Then every week became every week or two. This went on for two months.

Dennis's eyesight was continuing to improve. He went home to see his family and was preparing to leave the service. His papers were coming along fine, but I hadn't heard anything about mine. It seemed I was going to spend the rest of my life in this room with a light bulb and a toilet. There was nothing positive going on in my life at all. My wife and child were 1,500 miles away and I didn't know what I was going to do.

When Dennis came back from leave he wanted to have his eye checked. His eyesight was improving but a spot had suddenly appeared. The next day he was taken down to the eye clinic and brought back to the room and put on bed rest with the sandbags next to his head. They thought his retina was beginning to detach. I asked if he could see and Dennis said yes, but there was just this black thing in his vision. "Well, jeez, these guys fixed you once — they'll fix this," I told him. He seemed reassured, but I was still in the same state. Dr. Carney thought a visit home would help, so I was sent home again on another thirty-day leave.

When I got back Dennis's retina had detached. Just a day or two earlier they had done an operation called a belt. His eye was bandaged and he was back in bed with the sandbags around his head. It didn't look good, but I tried to assure him that everything would be fine, and to hang in there.

The next day I was called down to see Dr. Carney. Still no change. I could see the same fuzzy light and the hand blocking the light, but that was all. I went back to my room and sat there. I was starting to get depressed. Things were not changing. I began to ask myself, What are you going to do if this is the way you have to spend the rest of your life? I had to do something. I couldn't live here and just go home for occasional thirty-day leaves.

I sat there for hours thinking, What are you going to do for the rest of your life? Man, it was crazy. All kinds of thoughts would go through my head. Maybe you could do this, maybe you could do that. Well, you can't do that blind — there is just no way. Dennis wasn't doing well either. It didn't look like his operation was successful. He was blind again. It was really tough — the two of us in that room, both blind.

We had each other to talk to, and a few friends who had gotten their sight back would come and visit, but we both missed our families and knew this could not go on. Finally we were taken to some meetings with the Veterans Administration to begin to process us out of the Army.

I had no idea what I was going to do but I was told "Don't worry, the VA will take care of you." One of the leaders was also a blinded veteran. He showed us a Braille watch, something neither of us had ever seen. It was absolutely fantastic. We could actually tell what time it was by pushing a button to open the lid and then "reading" the hands with our fingers. We hadn't known what time it was for months. It was encouraging to both of us to know there were things out there to help us lead a normal life.

There were three blind schools: one in Hines, Illinois, another in Connecticut, and another in Palo Alto, California. We would probably be sent to Palo Alto because we were both from the West Coast. I asked the leader about "blind school." He explained that it is a school to help rehabilitate you. They teach you how to use a cane, how to get around, how to type, to use a telephone, to tell time with Braille watches, to use tools again, to cook, to lay out your clothing — basically how to live as a blind person. We both needed this. Both of us were just above the caveman stage.

We were eating with our fingers, and we were as crude as two people could possibly be. During one visit from Dennis's mother we were served our dinner but neither of us would eat. She asked us why we weren't eating.

"Mom, we can't eat in front of you," Dennis told her. "We can't see what we're eating, so the only way to eat is to put your finger in it and try it. If you like it, eat it. If you don't, move on to something else on your plate."

"Well, maybe I'd better leave for a while and come back later," she suggested.

"That would be great," Dennis told her, "or neither of us will get anything to eat."

A meeting was set up with a rehabilitation counselor whose name burns in my mind to this very day. There is a special place in hell for this guy. I was never so upset with anything in my life. After Dennis and I had sat for months thinking of what we wanted to do with the rest of our lives, this person told us very plainly that anything we wanted to do would be with his permission only. If we didn't want to do what he wanted, we would not be allowed to go to school or have any rehab at all.

He would ask us rudimentary questions, and if we didn't have the right answers, well that was too bad. We wouldn't get anything. In one meeting this counselor asked a veteran who had lost both his legs what he wanted to do with the rest of his life. The man replied that he had given it a lot of thought and since he was good with figures and had gotten A's in math he wanted to be a CPA. No, he was told. You scored really high on the mechanics part of the test. I think you need to be an auto mechanic. It was the most asinine thing I ever heard. How could he to do this with no legs?

Dennis and I were next. He asked us what we wanted to do.

"I want to go into range management," Dennis said.

"That is absurd," he was told. "You can't do that — you're blind. You can't see anything." When asked what I wanted to do I said I was raised on a farm and I thought I would like to farm the ocean and be a marine biologist, or work in a fishery somehow.

"You can't do that," I was told. "You are blind. What you two need to do is go back to your hometowns and go to the Federal building, courthouse, or post office and apply for a canteen vendor license. The building would be given to you so you would have no competition. You could go in there and sell magazines, pencils, and cigarettes. Run a small business from that location."

We were crushed. Dennis was twenty-two years old, I was twenty-one, the VA had said they were going to help us and now we were given this line of bullshit. It was simply unreal. We were both upset, but Dennis just sat there in silence. He didn't blow up like I did. I was madder than hell, yelling and screaming when we got back to the room. When the nurses learned what had happened they were angry, too.

I went down to the eye clinic and told the doctor, "Enough is enough. I want to go home." He arranged a thirty-day leave and I went back to my room and packed my belongings. The nurse got me a plane ticket and I was out of there.

Back in Santa Paula I explained to Anita what had happened.

"Well, maybe you ought to listen to him," she suggested.

"I can't do something like that — there is no way in the world I can do that," I said. I was just too young; all hope had been lost.

"Well, what are you going to do?" Anita asked. I didn't know. I just didn't know. The government couldn't help while I was home on leave, but I thought maybe someone could so I wrote to Congressman Charles Teague, the representative from my wife's home district. I explained the situation and told him I just wanted out of the Army. I couldn't take going back and forth anymore, and having my paperwork lost again. I just wanted to get a normal life, blind or not.

At the end of my thirty-day leave I returned to Fitzsimmons Hospital. As usual I went to the eye clinic and talked to Dr. Carney. I told him it wasn't working — I was not responding to treatment. I told him I simply wanted to get on with my life and I knew it was hard for him to tell someone that they were blind so I was saving him the trouble. I wanted to go home and go to blind school and learn how to be blind. Maybe someday there would be something or someone who could help me, but right now this is what I needed to do. He said that was something he could do for me.

Dennis had learned they were going to try something else to get his eyesight back. I told him with any luck they'll be able to help you. I don't have a chance anymore, I told him. There is nothing they can do for me. The next day I was put on an air ambulance and sent to Travis Air Force Base to wait for someone from the Blind Rehabilitation Center in Palo Alto to come and get me.

Chapter 3

Learning to 'See'

Early Monday morning a man came to pick me up for the sixty- or seventy-mile drive from Travis Air Force Base to the blind school in Palo Alto, California. The driver asked me about how I was hurt and reassured me that I had made the right decision to come to blind school. He said I would be 100% rehabilitated once I finished school. It was exactly what I needed to hear. After all the trouble at Fitzsimmons I really needed an uplift in my life.

When we arrived at the school I took the man's arm and he led me to the office and placed me in a chair. After awhile I heard a tapping on the floor and then someone said my name.

"I'm right here," I answered, and a figure with a cane moved toward me.

"Hi, I'm Gene Apple and I run this place," he said. "I would like to have a talk with you." He told me to get up and grab his arm, which I did. He then walked down the hallway toward his office with me in tow. We went into his office where he placed me in a chair and then walked around his desk and sat down perfectly. He asked me about my accident and I told him about the explosion and my stay at Fitzsimmons Hospital. He told me not to worry, that by the time I left I would be as proficient as I was before I was blind. I didn't know how this was possible but I was ready for anything.

Mr. Apple laid out the course plan for me and what I would be learning. Then he picked up the phone and called the receiving desk and a woman came in and ushered me up to my new room.

It was a small room with a bed and a dresser, but it had a window. I opened it and I could hear cars going by, smell the fresh air and hear the birds singing. This was a lot better than the hospital. After I got settled in I located everything in my room so I wouldn't trip. I even found the pictures on the wall as I got a feel for the room. Then I sat down on the bed and wondered what was next.

A few minutes later I heard a knock on the door. I answered it, and a man introduced himself.

"Hi, my name is Matt Angus and I am your mobility instructor. It is my job to teach you how to get around with a cane, so that you can go anywhere you want." We are starting right now, he added.

Things are sure moving fast, I thought. "What are we going to do?" I asked.

"I want you to come out into the hall," Matt said as he helped me walk out. "Our first lesson is going to be trailing. I want you to reach out with your fingertips and touch the wall." I did as he said. "I want you to walk down the hall with the back of your hand on the wall. You can find doors that way and also where the end of the room is. Then you can turn and go down the other side and find the stairwell. Go past it and find your way back to your room. You count the doors as you go so you can find the right door."

I did what he said. I began walking down the hall, found the doors and made the circle back to my room. This was the first time I had been able to leave my room without help and find my way back. I felt like I'd been let out of prison. After showing me the rest of the floor and where the bathrooms and the showers were, it was time for dinner.

"I will take you to dinner the first few days, but after that you'll have to find your own way," Matt explained. I would have to go to the mess hall and take meals like I did in the service. He took me down the stairs and around the corner and then outside. We walked out across the sidewalk to the car and drove to the mess hall. He took me inside and told me there was a handrail that went down the wall, then I would get to a counter where the servers would ask me if I wanted this or that. I would choose and they would put the food on a tray. You would continue down the line and over to the tables off to the left. It was up to you to find a place to sit. This seemed like an awful process the first few times. I didn't think I would be able to do it, but after the first few days it became second nature.

There were about twenty other men at the school and during meals or between classes we became friendly, helping each other through the process. Most of the men were older. They had been blinded in World War II and had toughed it out for years, then realized they needed rehabilitation. I guess I was lucky to go to the school right from the hospital.

Later that night as I lay in bed I realized I had made a lot of progress in just one day. I could go get something to eat, find my way around, open the window and smell the fresh air. Things were looking up.

The second day dawned with Matt knocking on my door to take me to breakfast. After breakfast we came back to the hall and he told me I would have a full slate of classes that day: mobility class, then correspondence class to learn how to type and use tape recorders and other machines to help you communicate. Then I will come get you and take you to manual dexterity classes where they will teach you how to use your hands and fingers, he said. After that I will take you to Braille class where you will learn Braille and how to label cans and things you use so you can identify them. After that you will go to home living class where you learn household skills such as doing your own laundry, making your bed, cooking your meals and eating with utensils instead of fingers.

I was so excited that I couldn't get to class fast enough. I would sit in my room at night and practice typing. I became very good at that. When I left the school I could type seventy words a minute. After two months of classes twice a day I was interviewed by Dr. Howard Glass. He saw that I was progressing rapidly and asked if I was interested in furthering my education and having some kind of professional rehab. Yes, I told him, I had a wife and small child and I wanted to go to college and further my education.

During three days of interviews Dr. Glass would ask questions and I would answer. Grading took about a week, and then I was called into his office and told I would be able to go to college. When he asked what I wanted to do I told him I wanted to farm the ocean. This was a tall order, but he thought it was possible. He himself had gone to school and gotten a degree, and he didn't think I would have a problem.

It was so exciting to have someone believe in me and give me hope. The staff at the blind school offered to help me any way they could. My communication and Braille teachers gave me a typewriter, Braille machine, tape recorder, dictating machine and all the things I needed to communicate in school with written correspondence.

The order was filled out and sent to the VA for approval and the next weekend I flew home to Santa Paula to see Anita. The flight from San Jose to L.A. was only nineteen dollars in those days. I went home and told Anita my paperwork was filled out and I was ready to go to school. I was going to get an education. She was so excited — we both thought things were going to get better. The world was at my feet. I just knew it.

We found a three-bedroom house near the universities and I used my GI bill to get the loan. We put down a small down payment and started the paperwork. I went back to school to finish my classes.

I was getting around very well. When Matt would take me to town I could find an address or go anywhere with my cane. I was becoming a human being again. After four months at the blind school I flew home for my twenty-second birthday. It was almost impossible for me to leave. I was so homesick, and I missed my wife and my daughter. I had only seen Heidi about three months of the first year of her life.

Back at the school I went to talk to Dr. Apple. I told him I wanted to go home, that I missed my family too much. "I understand," he told me, "but you have to pass a mobility test before you can leave. Let me talk to Matt and see how you are doing."

I was called back the next day. Dr. Apple told me Matt felt that I was ready for my final exam. This consisted of walking out of the building, crossing the street, getting on a city bus, going to the train station and getting on a train to San Francisco. There I had to get on a cable car on Powell Street, then go to Fisherman's Wharf and meet Matt for lunch at Tarantino's Restaurant. After lunch I had to make the return trip. If I could do this with no help from Matt I could go home.

After two days of intensive training Matt handed me money, train tickets and passes for the cable car. "I'll see you at lunch," he said, and off I went.

I took the bus to the train station, found the right train, boarded and found a seat and got off in San Francisco. The cable car was two blocks away, so I had to ask for directions. I got there, found a seat and rode to Fisherman's Wharf, although the cable car doesn't go all the way — it stops three blocks from the wharf. I asked directions from someone on the street and made my way to the restaurant. Matt and I had lunch.

I was on top of the world. After lunch Matt said, "I'll see you back at the school," and away I went. I made the same trip back, got off the bus at the school and walked through the door.

"You did pretty well," Matt said.

"Are you here already?" I was amazed. He'd been behind me the whole time. We went into Dr. Apple's office and sat down. When Matt told him I had done it Dr. Apple said, "Well John, I guess you will be leaving us."

The next two days were spent saying good-bye to my teachers and getting my stuff together and ready for school, plus a solemn good-bye to Dr. Glass who meant so much to my future and had gone above the call of duty to help me. I boarded a plane and headed home. I was back among the living. Blind school had been a godsend — sure, I had some problems but nothing I couldn't overcome. Some things were easy, some were hard. I figured they would all get easy as time went on. Soon my prosthetics and the typewriter and all the other equipment began to arrive.

Anita and I spent Christmas of 1969 in our own home with our baby. We were tremendously happy about our future and what 1970 would bring. All the bad luck was behind us.

Soon after the New Year Anita expressed her desire to have another child. I had just arrived home from blind school and wasn't sure I was ready for such a big step, but I was thrilled by this sign of Anita's commitment. It meant that, despite all we had been through, and all the uncertainty ahead, that nothing had changed between the two of us. Her commitment was unwavering, and she wanted us to have a family. I was out of the Army and going to school, and my pension would be coming through to supplement the meager Social Security disability we were living on. It seemed that things would be all right, so we decided to expand our family.

Every day we checked the mail for my paperwork for school and my Veteran's pension. Finally, in early January, a letter came. When Anita started to read it I could not believe what I was hearing. The VA on December 18, 1969, had rated me only ninety percent disabled. This meant I was to get only sixty-five percent of the benefits I was entitled to. I could not believe it. Anita looked at me and said, "What are we going to do?" The only thing I could think of was to write Congressman Teague again, so I dictated and Anita wrote the letter.

Congressman Teague immediately took up the case. I explained that I was released from the Army without a physical and my now my disability rating had came through at only ninety percent. After all the hospitalizations, losing one eye, only able to see light out of the other, and then completing blind school, how could they say I was not disabled?

Congressman Teague agreed. He talked to the VA and set up a physical exam, then we waited for a new decision on my benefits. Meanwhile, I received a letter from the rehabilitation board and was to go to the regional office in Los Angeles. There I was told I would have to take the rehabilitation examinations again. I explained that I had already taken this examination at the blind school and passed with flying colors. Dr. Glass had filed a report saying that I had passed the exam and had the ability to go to college. "Well," I said, "if that is the way it has to be, I will take the examination again." So Anita and I spent another three days getting up at five o'clock and driving to Los Angeles for the day-long exams.

It would take a week to ten days to evaluate my test results. Anita and I talked as we drove home. She asked how I did on the test, and I told her I thought I did fine. I remembered a lot of the questions and answered them the same way as before.

For the next week we stayed at home, waiting to hear the results. As time went on I began to get nervous. I had expected to start school in January and now, in mid-February, I wasn't any closer. I knew the soonest I could get into school would be the summer session in June.

We received a letter from the rehabilitation specialist ordering us to Los Angeles. I went into my interview and waited. The man entered and sat down and shuffled through some papers. He said he had learned a lot about me from my tests. I told him I was glad, maybe we were on the same ground. He said it was apparent I was ideal for outside work. I agreed. I was used to being outside and didn't think I would be capable of working at a desk. He said my test showed that and asked about my interests. I told him I wanted to farm the ocean. I wanted to go to school on the coast and learn how to harvest fish, shellfish — anything like that. That is simply not possible, he told me. You could never do the lab work or the other work involved.

Instantly I realized I was hearing the same things as I did in Denver. I asked what he thought I was capable of doing.

"Well," he replied, "I have been looking things over and I feel you should be a tour guide in a national park." Imagine: I couldn't do the lab work for a marine biologist but I could take sighted people through a national park. When they asked, What kind of tree is that? I wouldn't even know what they were pointing to. I had never heard anything so ridiculous in my life, and I told him so.

"You will either do it my way or no way," he replied. "There has to be a job at the end of this."

"I heard the same thing from some son of a bitch in Denver," I said, "and if it's your way or no way then it's no way. I will do it myself." I stood up, walked out of the room, got my wife and we left.

On the drive home I realized the VA's rehabilitation program was nothing but a cruel hoax. I was being led down the same path as before. My entire future had been taken from me, and they were still trying to fight me over my pension. I decided there was no future with this organization. All the people were the same and none of them benefited me.

Weeks went by with me stewing around, trying to figure out my future. Anita was pregnant with our second child, my compensation was still at ninety percent disability, and I was waiting to hear from Congressman Teague. Finally in late March I received a letter. My benefits had come through at one hundred percent disability. Congressman Teague had come through. I was going to get what was coming to me.

Still, I grew restless. I needed something to do. Sometimes I would mow the lawn three times a day just for something to do. Over and over I would get the lawn mower out, run it around and put it back. I was slowly going nuts. I didn't know what I was going to do.

In April Anita proposed a trip to Grants Pass, Oregon, to visit my grandparents. They had never seen Heidi, for Anita and Heidi had always stayed in Santa Paula with her mother.

When we reached Southern Oregon I felt like I was coming home. I knew what I wanted to do. I wanted to come back to Oregon and farm again. After a few days Anita said she had fallen in love with it, too. All the trees and surrounding areas were beautiful, the wood smoke from the mills in town, all of it. I broached the question: "Would you consider living here?" When Anita said yes I told her I wanted to move here and raise our children as I was raised — on a farm, with work ethics and morals to make real people out of them.

My family had come here on the Oregon Trail, and I wanted my children to grow up here. I knew I was never going to college, so we had better enjoy the rest of our lives. Our most important job now was raising our children.

We bought a newspaper and looked through the real estate ads. We found a few places we wanted to see, and on the third trip — always the charm — we found a beautiful ranch-style home with three bedrooms, two baths, a large kitchen, family room and living room, a two-car garage, and — the best part — an acre of land, fenced, with a barn. I could go outside and work and never worry about getting lost. I would always be inside the fence.

We both decided this was home and immediately put a small down payment on the land to start the paperwork. I told my grandmother the soil was in my veins, and I was coming home. Anita and I went back to Santa Paula and put our house on the market. We were moving to Oregon.

Anita's parents were disappointed, but they understood that I needed something to do, and going to school in California was not an option anymore. Within two weeks we had a buyer for our home and notified the VA that I was moving to Oregon. On July 1, 1970, we loaded the car with our belongings and made our way up Interstate 5 to Grants Pass and our new home.

Chapter 4

A Fifth-Generation Oregonian Returns Home

We arrived in Grants Pass and made our way seventeen miles south to a little town called Williams, where my mother and stepdad lived. We were going to stay with them until our furniture arrived.

Little Heidi was just amazed. She had always been in the city so she had never seen so many big trees and animals before. My mom had cows and sheep, and there were a lot of wild deer and birds around. Heidi was overwhelmed at first, but she quickly grew to like the animals. She discovered that the sheep would let her pet them and the cows would stand still if she fed them. She spent a lot of time standing at the fence, feeding grass to the cows, one blade at a time. One day we visited my grandmother, and I took Heidi to see the chicken coop in the back yard. It was the first time she had seen chickens, and when I explained that's where eggs come from she thought it was the neatest thing.

Heidi was very active at twenty months old and wanted to run and play a lot. My mother had a small house so we spent a lot of time outside with Heidi, trying to wear her out so she would sleep at night. Soon our furniture was delivered and Anita and I got our family settled into our new home. There was only one problem: we didn't have any animals. Heidi always wanted to go to my mother's or grandmother's to see the animals. The chickens were her favorite.

One afternoon I was listening to the bargain roundup on a local radio station. They were advertising bantam chickens for fifty cents apiece, so I wrote down the number and called. When we got there Heidi was delighted — there were chickens everywhere. We picked out some chickens and a small rooster, which she immediately named Cock-a-doo. We brought them home and let them loose in the barn. Heidi was fascinated, watching them run around. They also had a purpose — eating earwigs and bugs in the barn. The house had been vacant for a year and a half so I had been concerned about insect bites when Heidi came with me to the barn.

Across the street about a half a block away there was a little store that sold gas and dry goods, soda and other convenience items. I purchased some chicken scratch and showed Heidi how to feed the chickens. She thought this was the best thing of all, and soon we had the fattest banty chickens in all of Southern Oregon. We had to make at least fifteen trips a day to the barn to feed the chickens. Heidi would throw the corn and the chickens would eat and scratch. The rooster would crow and Heidi would throw her head back and yell "cock-a-doo, cock-a-doo, cock-a-doo!"

Holly and Heidi delighted in feeding the animals. Their fun was my education, as they guided me around our farm.

Soon I realized all those trips to the barn had helped me learn the way and recognize where I was by the shade of the trees. Heidi didn't know that what was great fun to her was actually my education. She was the best Seeing Eye guide anyone could have.

Heidi was my constant companion. She would say "I have to go, Daddy. You will get lost without me," not realizing how right she was. It soon became apparent that I had to do some work in the barn without Heidi or she would have to learn to stay in one place. I had to know where she was so I didn't hurt her. I would say "Can you stand still right here for me?" and she would always say yes. Failure to do so would result in having to stay in the house with her mother, looking out the window. She didn't like this. It took only two or three times for her to learn that she had to mind me. A few years later I overheard Heidi tell her little sister, "Holly you have to stay here. Dad is depending on us."

I spent the summer cleaning up the place. I mowed the lawn by setting up picnic benches in grids and mowing in the grid until I hit a bench. Then I would get on my hands and knees to make sure I got it all cut, then I moved the grid. I quickly learned by the shade of the trees and the house how big the area was I was mowing so I was able to make the grid bigger.

After getting the dead limbs out of the trees and the lawn mowed I began to look at the fences. I decided that if I was going to run this farm I was going to have to learn how to drive nails. Remembering when I could see this didn't seem like a problem, but just try to drive a nail with your eyes closed. The result is a lot of lost fingernails, and many bruises and cuts. You must realize that when you are blind it is impossible to wear gloves to do anything. You have to be able to see and you "see" through your hands. For thirty years my hands took a terrible beating. I would set up boards in the garage and start lightly at first, tapping the nail then putting my hand up to check my progress. It was hard to hold a hammer after the loss of my right thumb. I had to wrap my index finger around the hammer, then grasp the handle with my other three fingers. This caused the hammer to be at a weird angle at times. I had to learn to turn my wrist so the hammer would strike flat, but with practice I became very proficient. Some twenty years later my skill with a hammer caused the carpenter building my home to lose his job. The contractor drove up the driveway and watched me put siding on the shop I was building with my friend while they were building my house. The owner of the company walked up to the carpenter and said "Buddy, look at that man," pointing at me. "He's blind and he can work faster than you. I think it's time for you to get your lunch bucket and go home."

I have driven hundreds of pounds of nails in my life, and Heidi was a real help, believe it or not. Remember the small child's toy with the little hammer and pegs? You pound the pegs through to the other side, then flip it over and start again. Heidi and I would play this for hours. She would do one side, then turn it over and give it to me to do the other side. Back and forth we went, and I got better and better at hammering.

I was once asked, "Don't you hit your fingers?"

"Well, sure," I replied. "Don't you hit yours?"

With early fall came the arrival of my second daughter, born September 12, 1970. I named her Holly Bryanna Malkow, and she was the highlight of our lives. Our family was complete now, with two beautiful children. After Holly's arrival, Anita's father, Lloyd Johnson, came to see his new grandchild and was amazed at all I had accomplished, although he could see a lot that needed to be done. As Lloyd helped me he tried to figure out ways to teach me how to do things. This became a job that lasted about six years. When Thanksgiving came and it was time for him to go home he didn't want to leave. He enjoyed his grandchildren and his only daughter lived some 800 miles away from him. After talking it over, Anita and I asked Lloyd to live with us. He agreed. He had been a carpenter all his life, and there were a lot of things he could show me to help me get along. Lloyd had all the tools to build a house, and he could show me how to use them safely.

Whenever anyone was willing to show me how to do things, I was willing to learn, so Anita took her dad back to Santa Paula to get his belongings — most importantly, his tools — and bring him back to Southern Oregon.

One afternoon in late November there was a knock at the door. Anita answered it to find a man in a suit standing there.

"Hi," he said. "My name is John Mosiani and I am a social worker for the VA. It's my job to make sure that John is getting on in life." Anita came and got me, and we sat down at the kitchen table. He began to tell me about all the programs available to me from the Veterans Administration. I told him I would take any help, but I would not go through what I did with my schooling. The regional office was in Portland, over 300 miles from my home, so he thought it was just as well that I settled in here. After some coffee and an assurance that he would be back in early spring, Mr. Mosiani left.

I spent a lot of time with my father-in-law, learning how to measure wood using notches and then cutting the wood. We made rabbit hutches by sawing and cutting boards with handsaws and then nailing them together. With the hutches made we had to have some rabbits. Again we listened to the radio program and soon we had rabbits as well as chickens. Heidi liked feeding the rabbits. Twice a day, every day, I would lift her up to the hutches so she could feed and pet them.

That spring my uncle offered to buy two wiener pigs if we would raise them. He would keep one and we could have the other. This was a fine idea, except that we didn't have a hog pen. So Anita's dad and I found a place on the property to build a hog barn. We took the measurements, went to the lumberyard and got to work. In nothing flat we had a proper hog barn. We were just putting on the roof when Anita came down with Heidi and Holly and saw me standing there with blood dripping down my arm and a huge smile on my face, holding a roofing nail between my thumb and pinkie finger. I had knocked all the ends off my index, ring and middle fingers. Lloyd had asked me if I wanted help and I had told him no, this was my project.

When the barn was finished my uncle showed up with two hogs, about fifty pounds apiece. This was something curious to Heidi; she had never seen a pig before. I told her they were just like our family dog, Rafe.

"What do you mean?"

"They just sound different," I told her. "Rafe barks and they squeal."

Now along with the chickens and rabbits we had pigs to feed. This became a twenty-year love affair for our entire family. Heidi loved to watch them eat. She would throw her head back and laugh. I can remember watching her when she was in high school, doing the same thing. Soon we added some laying hens for eggs, and a baby calf — a real treat for Heidi, who got to bottle-feed it three times a day. Heidi would hold the bottle and the calf would suck it greedily as she laughed and talked to it.

Next I needed to plant a garden, but first I had to till the ground — a new challenge. I went into town and purchased a five-horsepower front wheel tiller, guaranteed to dig up any dirt in Southern Oregon. My grandfather and I took it home and after I staked the ground I brought out the tiller and pulled the cord. The engine came to life. I placed the tiller in gear and heard Anita and her father laughing as the tiller began jerking around. When Lloyd got the same result we were forced to turn off the machine and read the directions. It would have been better to do that before we started the engine, but we discovered the tiller worked easier with the drive peg down, causing the tines to dig. I adjusted the depth of the pegs, then restarted the tiller and put it in gear.

It was a little rough. The soil in our garden spot hadn't been worked in many years, some parts never at all. Anita walked behind me and her father walked in front, yelling "Left!" or "Right!" Anita would pull my shirt left or right so I knew how to follow a straight line. After a day and a half we had a properly tilled garden. Everyone was happy as we seeded the garden with Holly in the playpen watching and Heidi helping me plant onions. Lloyd planted the carrots and radishes as the seeds were too fine for me to hold.

The spring rains came and the garden grew. Soon it was time to harvest, and Anita no longer had to buy vegetables at the store. We were growing our own, fresh from the garden to the table. The hens were laying eggs, and soon we had so many eggs we started selling them to the neighbors. The chickens were paying for themselves. We thought this was heavenly. The pigs had grown and we butchered them. Now we didn't have to buy as much meat at the store. Our calf was growing and we could see roast, steak and hamburger ahead. It didn't take long to figure out how much we were saving by growing our own food. For the first time we had money for a few extras. We didn't have a lot of money — just enough to get by. My social security disability and pension were not meant to fund a lavish lifestyle.

When Mr. Mosiani returned I showed him all I had accomplished with the garden and the pigpen, and Lloyd showed him how he was teaching me to use tools. At the end of our conversation he asked if I would consider going to school. I said I would love to go to school but I would not be treated like I was before. I could not handle the letdown again. Mr. Mosiani promised to see what he could do.

I could hardly believe how fast Heidi and Holly were growing. Already Holly was able to sit up and crawl around. My family was growing. Anita and I were very much in love and enjoying our simple life, and the days passed quickly.

Our farm was growing, too. I purchased two hogs and we took in a neighbor's horse because our calf couldn't eat all the grass in the pasture. Our chickens, rabbits and laying hens were all doing fine. Early spring and summer were simply gorgeous that year. Rain two or three days, then seventy degrees for a day or two — just enough to keep everything green and watered. When we drove the seventeen miles to my mother's house Anita always remarked about how green everything was compared to her home in Santa Paula. In the San Gabriel Mountains of California the grass was only green three or four weeks of the year, in the very early spring. Then it would dry out and turn brown for the rest of the year. Anita fell in love with Southern Oregon. She loved the green trees and the Rogue River that ran through town.

It seemed there was always something going on in our community. I encouraged Anita to find something to do by herself, as we spent every day together. When my aunt invited her to go bowling Anita fell in love with it. Even today she bowls every Tuesday and Friday with her friends. It's her time away from me and the family. In all our years together we have never had a cross word with each other, not one. She has been my greatest cheerleader, always confident in my ability and always encouraging me to do the best I can. Anita had faith in me when no one else did.

In July Mr. Mosiani returned as promised and asked if I still wanted to go to school. Yes, I told him, if I could. When he said I would have to go to Portland and take the tests all over again I refused. I had been through that twice and I didn't feel the VA had my best interests at heart. Mr. Mosiani disagreed. He said he believed the tests would be able to tell me exactly what I could do. I didn't doubt that, I said. They would tell me what I could do, not what I wanted to do. He was sorry, he said, but he would have to take all the communication equipment, except the typewriter, with him when he left. I gathered up the equipment and gave it to him and when he drove away it lit a fire in my gut that still burns to this day. If the Veterans Administration was going to order me around and tell me what I could and couldn't do with the rest of my life I didn't need them. That day I swore to myself that I would become the greatest farmer I could be.

Summer turned to early fall, and it was time to replant the garden. We decided to expand the garden along the back of the house since it had done so well the previous year. Tilling the garden as I did before I noticed the trees and shade spots. I was able to navigate my way along the back of the house, kind of like a ship avoiding a lighthouse, moving in or out depending on the shade spots. Anita was still behind me tugging on my shirt and pulling to direct me when I went too far off course. We worked up both sides of the house, then we brought up manure and tilled that in. Each time it was becoming easier to till.

The cool, crisp fall brought back a lot of feelings from my youth. My father and I had done a lot of hunting during the fall, and I wanted to go hunting so badly. It was in my blood and now it was lost forever.

Another young couple, Bill and Charlene Madda, had moved into the house next door. Bill had just gotten out of the Navy, and they had a son five years old who became a playmate for Heidi. Now she didn't have to spend all her time with me — she could play with Johnny. We all became quick friends, having dinner and doing things together. As Bill became more at ease with me one day he said, "You do things I can't believe you do. Sometimes I can't believe you can't see." I told him that was the best compliment anyone had ever given me. I worked very hard to be that way. The world sees, and you have to make your place in it. You can't be blind all the time. I wanted to raise my children as normally as I possibly could.

Bill was a hunter as well and he knew what I was missing, so on opening day of deer season he asked me to go out with him in the truck. I was very excited — I couldn't wait to go. We drove out to a place called Taylor Creek and had a great time. We didn't see any deer, but we had lunch and just drove around. The pine scent in the air and the wind blowing in the trees — it was exactly as I remembered it. We went out every Saturday morning for the next three or four weeks. On the last trip of the season Bill saw a young forked horn buck. He leaned over the hood of the truck and shot and the buck dropped. He took me by the shoulder and said "Come on, I got it." When we got to the deer I put my hands all over it and felt it. I was just as excited as if I had shot it myself. I helped him drag it to the truck and load it up and we headed home. It was the end of the great season. We felt like Daniel Boone and Davy Crockett coming home with that deer. Bill shared the meat with us, but more importantly, I had found an out, something for me to do. I could go on these hunting trips with Bill and his other friends, and I seemed to fit in. When Bill's company transferred him to Pendleton I never saw him again, but he had given me a start. I felt I could enjoy the outdoors again.

In 1972 two people entered my life who meant the world to me. The first was Harry Johnson, a retired millwright who moved into the house next door. Harry was a character. He had spent his life in the mills in Oregon and could make anything. If I had problems with something and Lloyd couldn't help I would go next door and ask Harry. His answer was always the same.

"Someone built that, so we can fix that one or build another just like it." Those words stick in my mind to this day. Every time I find myself stuck I think of Harry and know I can either fix it or build one just like it. Harry was a huge influence in my life over the next five years. Harry would teach me steel and Lloyd would teach me wood.

The next person was Ed James, a real Wild West cowboy. He always told me he was in the last cow and sheep war in the state of Oregon over in Prineville. Ed had been a horse buckaroo most of his life and he was raising horses about a half-mile from our home. When the horse we were boarding got sick Ed came over. I watched him and listened to the way he talked to the horse, and later I asked him what he had done. He said the horse had colic and an eating disorder but a dose of mineral oil would fix it.

Ed began stopping by on his way to the store, and one day he asked me to go on a horseback ride with him. I hadn't ridden since I was blind, but Ed had an old mare that was very calm and would follow his horse so it would be safe. The next day he brought the horses and led me around to the side of one. I put my foot in the stirrup and my hand on the saddle horn and climbed up. We rode for hours, through the woods to the Applegate River and a long loop back. It was something I never thought I would be able to do again. I had a love for all kinds of animals, but this horse was special. We rode a couple times a week, and I eventually bought Sandy. We bred her and she had two foals so the children got to watch them grow up on the farm.

I had rehabilitated myself and tried to become more outgoing. This brought a lot of questions and comments, like "What do you have all over your face?" and "What in the world happened to you?" One day I was stopped outside the courthouse in Grants Pass by a police officer who told me I should wash my face before I came to town. This cut me very deeply, and I began to withdraw. The chemicals in my face were silver nitrate, the same thing that old black and white pictures were made from. Working outdoors in the sun had caused the chemicals to discolor my face in spots.

Another time in the store across the street a little boy asked his mother what was wrong with that man, pointing at me. She looked at me and told her son "That is just an old nigger." When she got closer and realized I had been in an accident the woman apologized, but it didn't help. First, I couldn't believe she would teach that bigotry to her child. Her words cut deep into my soul. Being blind was bad enough, but having these facial scars was worse. I had never seen them so I had no idea how bad they were.

At my next physical I asked the doctor if there was anything they could do for my face. He said it was something I would have to live with. They looked at my eye and again there was no hope. On the way home I told Anita we had to keep trying — we could never give up. I believed that someday we would hear the right answer.

That fall Anita's mother came to visit her grandchildren. Before she left she asked me what I wanted for my birthday in October. When I told her I wanted a chain saw she thought I was out of my mind — the same thing Anita had said. We had a fireplace and I had cut up all the wood on our place. We could have two or three cords of logs delivered for twenty dollars. I would have to cut the logs to fit the fireplace, but this would save a lot on our winter heating bills as well as give me something to do.

"I have never said no to you but I will not buy you a chain saw," my mother-in-law said, "but I will give you the fifty dollars to buy the saw." She tucked the money in a birthday card and Anita took me to the secondhand store where I had seen a beauty — a Pioneer with a twenty-inch bar. When I bought it and took it home everyone was terrified — everyone but me. Anita and her dad were sure I was going to cut off my foot or my hands. I told them I had run a saw when I could see and I could do it safely. Harry agreed. He didn't see any reason I couldn't run the saw as long as I felt the log on both sides and held onto the saw. "You're careful when you do things," he said.

The next day I ordered my first load of logs, and when they were delivered I set to work. I would saw three quarters of the way through a log, shut the saw off, roll the log over and check my spot, then start the saw and run it through the other side to complete the cut. It worked perfectly. I cut wood until the saw was dull. When Harry came over I asked him how to sharpen a chain. He told me it was going to be difficult, but it could be done. We sat down with the proper round file and he tried to show me how to sharpen the chain. I could not get the concept of sharpening the teeth with my eyes closed until Harry said, "John, I want you to think of this as a motorized chisel. You are trying to sharpen the top side of the teeth when you should be trying to sharpen the bottom side. Imagine this as a chisel that is on a chain that goes around and around and I think you can do it." Sure enough, I could. I have been sharpening that saw for over twenty-eight years — maybe not as well as the saw shop, but I can make it cut and cut straight.

With the all the wood cut into bolts standing on end my next challenge was splitting the wood. I got out a maul and a wedge, and I would sit on a round and tap the wedge in using the same technique as with nails. Then I would stand up and swing the maul to hammer the wedge in until the round was split, or until the wedge was buried and I would have to use another to split the wood apart. I broke a lot of handles but I had several mauls so when I broke one I would go and get another. At the end of the week I would spend the day reshaping the handles and reinserting them in the heads. I never gave up and I still make firewood to this day.

In late fall Mr. Mosiani made another stop at our house. We had received a letter from Social Security about a change in Medicare. I was eligible for part B Medicare but it would cost a monthly fee. When we asked about it Mr. Mosiani told us we didn't need this coverage because we already had insurance from the Veterans Administration and they would always take care of me. He also explained that the VA was changing the way social services worked. There was to be a division in every group office called the VIST program, the Visual Impairment Service Team, that would be my contact with the government. Years later these two programs were to have a huge impact on my life.

One day Anita came home from bowling very excited. The women at the bowling alley were going to form a fast pitch softball league.

"I want to play," she said. "I haven't played softball since I was in high school." It sounded like a lot of fun, so Anita tried out and made the team. All the husbands and fathers and kids were in the stands cheering. The gals were out there playing hard, some getting good hits, some striking out, but everyone having a good time. After the games on Tuesdays and Saturdays everyone would congregate at a local pizza place. It was a lot of fun for our family, and Anita played until the girls were out of high school. She played on a team with both of our daughters before she retired.

The team's pitcher was Robin Hutchinson. Her husband Kenny and I would sit together, talking about hunting and fishing trips. One day he asked if I wanted to go hunting with him. I told him when I had gone with Bill I had ridden in the truck and stayed on the roads, but Kenny said he could do better than that. He knew of some open areas that had been logged and he thought we could come up with a system so I could hunt also. At first I didn't think I could shoot a gun safely, but we figured out a way and I hunted blind for twenty-eight years. I never got any special licenses or hunted out of season. I would hold the gun while Kenny looked through the scope, and I would hold onto his shirt as we walked through the woods. He would give instructions like "Raise your foot, here comes a log," or "Duck, here comes a branch." Eventually he would just tap it lightly with his foot. We had no success hunting, but we had a good time. Kenny and I became as close as any two brothers could be. We think alike, act alike, and as we have grown older we even look alike.

The routine things on the farm went on. Calves grew into cows and the vegetables were harvested and canned. Summer turned to fall and it was time for Heidi to start school. She was so excited to wear her new school clothes and go out and get on the bus every morning. Heidi was smart as a whip and always had been. She would come home from school and set up a box like a desk and teach Holly everything she had learned in school that day. Holly would listen and stare at Heidi as if she were in school, trying very hard to do what Heidi was teaching her. Heidi was patient with her little sister, and Holly would do it over and over until she got it right. When Heidi was away at school each day Holly came along to work with me just as Heidi had done when she was little. I really loved my children.

In the fall of 1973 I was called to Portland for my annual physical exam. Once again they examined my eye and saw no hope, and I asked about my face but was told nothing could be done. And once again on the way home I told Anita there would come a time when they would give me the right answers.

Shortly after that I learned there was a new plastic surgeon in Grants Pass — an ear, nose and throat specialist who was also a facial plastic surgeon. I was so sensitive about the comments made about my face that I made an appointment with Dr. Mike Wheatley.

I told him about the accident that had left silver nitrate in my face, and I related the story of the policeman telling me, in front of my wife, to wash my face before I came to town. Dr. Wheatley listened with interest and began rubbing my face and feeling the texture of it. He didn't know how deep the chemicals were but he said "I think we may be able to do some good." He described a procedure called dermabrasion — actually the sanding of your face — that might remove some of the discoloration.

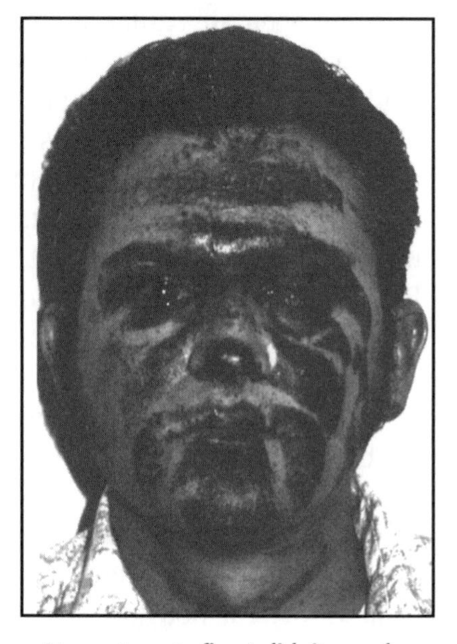

At age twenty-five I didn't see the extent to which my face caused stares and ridicule.

The first time the procedure was done under general anesthesia and he literally ground my face off. It was painful when I woke up, and I had a bad reaction to the anesthesia. It was like going back to the time of the explosion. It was so traumatic, we never used general anesthesia again. Dr. Wheatley would use a local anesthesia and keep me awake to grind my face off. Each time he left some pigment, because he didn't know how deep it went. He never gave up. "Well, maybe we'll get it all next time," he said. While it wasn't a hundred percent successful the comments lessened a little bit as it became obvious that I had been in an accident. My face was spotted — freckled, Dr. Wheatley used to say.

That spring I received a letter from the VA saying I would be assigned to a VIST coordinator, Miss Balloon. She visited and explained that everything would be the same except there would be no more home visits. I would have to go to Portland to meet with her when I went for my physicals.

The summer of 1975 was a very wet one in Oregon, causing the price of hay to go up over 300 percent. Having all the animals to feed became a tremendous financial burden, and we had to make some decisions. We could not afford all the animals anymore. We butchered the calf and sold the horses, as I couldn't afford to feed them. We waved good-bye to them as they left. It was especially sad to see Sandy go. She was good to me and the kids loved to ride her, but we simply could not afford to keep her.

That fall Anita's mother's health began to fail. This was very hard on Anita, an only child. Her father lived with us but her mother was 800 miles away. When Madge was hospitalized and Anita flew down to California the girls and I did all right on our own. They would stand on chairs next to me when I cooked — simple things like grilled cheese, soup or hot dogs, that I knew they would eat.

We spent Thanksgiving with Anita's mother's that year, and it was clear that she was not doing well so we persuaded her to come home with us for Christmas. The change of scenery and being with her grandchildren seemed to make her feel better, but right before Christmas she got worse and we had to take her to Medford to a heart specialist. They gave her a pacemaker, which seemed to help, but we were both worried about her. We loved Madge very much, but we could not afford for Anita to fly back to California every time her mother got sick. The best solution seemed to be to ask Anita's mother to move to Southern Oregon. Lloyd agreed. He felt he had helped me enough and he knew that Madge needed us more. Madge, however, absolutely refused to move into our home. She felt she needed privacy at times and so did we. But if we could find a place with two homes on it she would love to move to Oregon. She felt very far away from everyone, especially now that she was ill.

Finding a place turned out to be easy. Within two days our real estate agent had found three pieces of property. We ruled out the first two because they didn't have anything for me to do. The third was three miles out on Lower River Road. The house was on the river, with five acres of land and a barn. The fences needed repair, so I would have work to do. The best thing about this property was that it was 170 feet wide and over 1,400 feet deep, back to the Rogue River, with 500 feet of river frontage — an ideal fishing spot. And right next door was a mobile home park for seniors with new spaces for rent. This was exactly what we were looking for. We called Anita's mother and she was on the next plane to Oregon. We picked her up at the airport and brought her out for a look. It was perfect. We were close, and she could have a home and we could have a home with a larger farm. Madge put a down payment on a mobile home and went back to California and put her place up for sale. Her house sold right away, and our agent made an offer on our farm that we couldn't refuse. We bought the place at 4601 Lower River Road and on April 15, 1976, we moved into the home on the river where we raised our children until they left home.

Chapter 5

At Home in the Rogue Valley

Spring was the nicest in years. We had sunny days to plant our garden at our new home. I began to work on the fences, which were in such bad shape I eventually had to re-fence the entire place. I started with the front pasture to make sure our calf couldn't get out. Replacing the fence posts and wire took a lot of time. Next I began to work on the old barn. I would lay out a big project and a little project and start to work. Sometimes the larger projects took a couple days, as it took time to lay things out straight. Off the old barn was a hog house with a farrowing area. As I cleaned it up I realized it would be easy to keep a sow there, and I knew the girls would love to have pigs, with little ones coming all the time.

The man at the feed store happened to have a pig for sale on consignment. The owner had moved to Alaska and couldn't take it with her. "Rosy" had been raised like one of the family and was almost like a pet. She was a huge animal — more than 700 pounds — and just as docile as any dog could be. What a sweetie. It was an immediate love affair with all of us. We scratched up the $250 to buy Rosie and my brother-in-law helped me move her home. She was bred about two months and would have a litter of pigs in about six weeks. My children were excited. Rosie was so friendly, they could scratch her and play with her. I never had any problem with the kids when it was time to feed the animals. They loved to do it, but they both wanted to feed Rosy. Finally I had to divide the food so they could each feed her something, scratching her head while they poured the food in her trough.

The ditch walker had showed me how I could irrigate the property with flood irrigation. The water was pumped out of the Rogue River and came down a ditch that ran along the road. I simply blocked off the ditch and opened huge valves to release water onto my fields. This wasn't hard at all, but it was kind of scary at first because I thought I would get lost. The property was only 170 feet wide and 1,400 feet long, but it was divided into two pieces. The back part was divided into five long lanes with raised mounds to keep the water within the lanes. As I walked across the field I walked through the lanes that I could easily feel with my feet, so no matter where I was in the field I knew I was only eighty-five feet from a fence. I could walk down the lanes and stomp my feet in the water until there was no more water. That's how I knew where the water was and when to shut it off. After doing this several times I had a hay crop.

It was June, the weather was about eighty-five degrees and it was time to harvest the hay. The local ditch walker was also the hay man and did some custom cutting. He would come in and cut the hay, rake it, then bale it for a small price. My first crop was about 400 bales of hay, but it was out in the field. Getting it into the barn was a problem. It was just me and Anita and an old pickup truck, but we set to work. Anita would drive the truck and I would walk beside it, holding on to the tailgate. She stopped next to the bales and I would pick them up and put them on the back of the truck. When I had three bales in the truck I would climb up and stack them. I could get thirty-five bales in each load, then we would take it to the barn and stack it. I did this twice a year for fifteen years. You have no idea how much pride I felt when I looked at my first hay crop in the barn. I couldn't believe I had done it. It was grand to think that I could farm along with everyone else.

Trout season opened in May, and I was eager to teach my children how to fish. Heidi was seven now and Holly was five. I had bought an old riverboat a few years before and moved it down by the river. We got up early on opening day, and I cut six-foot willow switches like I had used when I was a child. I attached about eight feet of line, and at the end I tied a black fly with a red tail, the same fly I had used when I was young. I took the kids out in the boat and sat between them, and I showed them how to put the fly in the water and swing it back and forth behind the boat, taking turns one after another. The fish would dart out of the rapids and take the fly. It was so much fun. My daughters became such expert fishers I finally had to get a ruler and cut it at 10 inches. If the fish weren't longer than the ruler, I told them, we had to throw them back.

In June Rosy gave birth to our first litter of pigs. She had fourteen beauties, about equally males and females. We had pigs everywhere. They would squirm out under the gate and Rosy would oink and they would run back under the gate. It was fascinating for the kids, and we did so well we hoped to get into the business of raising our own and maybe selling the wiener pigs. I traded our first litter for a calf so now I had two cattle, and I had bartered some of the pigs for materials to build fences.

At the end of summer Rosy had another litter, so we had a barn full of hay and pigs. I still listened to my radio show every day and when winter came I realized there was a hay shortage, and I was able to trade hay for two heifer calves. Now my herd was four heifers, so we would be able to grow our own meat.

Farming is a very repetitious job. The same things are done every year. The animals are bred, hay is made and fences are maintained, because if there is a weak spot the pigs will find it and tear it up. They delight in watching you build something and then going over to see if they can tear it up. Every year, too, I ordered logs for firewood and made enough to fill a large woodshed. The wood stove was our only source of heat at the farm.

Those were good years for our family. Anita's mother's health had improved since her move to Oregon, and I think seeing her grandchildren every day helped. The VA caseworkers seemed to change frequently, but I was not called to Portland for physical exams. The Vietnam War was over and it seemed that the services for veterans weren't there.

In 1978 Heidi turned nine years old and could join 4-H, something she had been looking forward to since we bought Rosy. We went to the first meeting and became very involved as 4-H parents in a farming community. Heidi purchased her first hog from her 4-H leader and learned about the record-keeping and preparations for the fair in August. She did so well feeding her hog that by June it was the weight it should have been in August. We didn't know there was a weight criteria, so we showed up with a grand champion pig two months before the fair and had to get a replacement. As with everything, her first year was a learning experience.

At the first meeting of Heidi's second year in 4-H I was asked to be a leader and help out with my expertise with hogs. I hesitated, not knowing how the other kids in the club would relate to me. My kids were used to my being blind, but they had been around it all their lives. The kids in the club knew I was blind, but I wasn't sure if they could adjust. It would be quite an undertaking for me. I wouldn't know if the kids were absorbing what I was telling them about raising and breeding hogs because I couldn't see their faces. I eventually said yes to becoming a 4-H leader because I felt I had a lot to offer.

Heidi got two pigs that year. One was a barrow, a castrated male pig, and the other was a gilt, a young female pig, which she was going to raise as a sow. The meetings went off and I didn't have problems with the kids, nor did they have problems adjusting to me. We had about seventeen or eighteen kids in the club and we all got along. Frank Potts, the other leader, would fill in the gaps when the kids weren't paying attention. He was my eyes during the five years we spent as 4-H leaders.

This time Heidi had learned the rules and learned them well. She met the weight criteria and went to the fair. Her barrow took a first place ribbon and she did quite well at the auction at the end of fair. Her gilt was champion of the gilts and overall reserve champion female. She was being rewarded for all her years of work in learning how to raise pigs.

Next year it was Holly's turn. She also overfed her pig and had to take a replacement to the fair. But her second year she took two hogs and, like Heidi, took champion gilt and reserve champion female at the fair. The girls had walls of ribbons from their years in 4-H.

Dr. Wheatley had ground my face off one more time in 1977. He didn't think he could do anymore because it was just too deep. He suggested trying an acid treatment, called a chemical peel, around my eyes. In this procedure, acid was applied to my face for about twenty minutes, causing the skin to fall off two or three days later. It was not very successful. The tattooing was too deep and it was an extremely painful process. It was only supposed to burn for twenty minutes, but it would burn with intense pain for twelve hours or more. So Dr. Wheatley decided to cut out some of the discoloration. He did a wonderful job; the surgery left no scars. He cut a large piece off my neck and sewed it up without the black stains. He cut the outside of my lips, which were also jet black, and pulled the inside skin out, then reattached it to the outside skin.

The surgery was successful in the areas where he removed the black, but it didn't do a complete job. I had undergone five dermabrasions, but my face was still badly scarred and tattooed. Dr. Wheatley didn't tell me this, though. He told me "We made quite a difference to your face and you have to think of it as freckled." I thought OK, I could live with freckles. This did a lot for my mental acceptance of what my face looked like. Dr. Wheatley had really helped me come out of my shell. Before, I had been pretty reclusive. I didn't have many friends, just the ones who accepted me. But when we went out eventually someone would make a comment about my face and I would withdraw again. Working with the 4-H kids helped me get over these feelings as much as I helped them. There would always be people who made comments about my face, but nothing more could be done. Technology had to catch up. Dr. Wheatley said if my face gradually got darker he would grind it off again, and that he would call me if new treatments became available. Taking this as a finish from the doctor I started living my life again and waiting for new developments in facial plastic surgery.

It would take nearly twenty years for the new technology to come along. Meanwhile, in 1986 Dr. Wheatley was diagnosed with pancreatic cancer and the following year my friend and doctor succumbed to this disease. For many years afterwards I felt I had no one to help me.

Through the years our farm developed and our animals grew. I had a few sows and a nice herd of cattle. When my neighbor had a registered Hereford bull and two registered cows for sale Anita's mother purchased them for me, knowing we couldn't afford it but we needed a bull to breed our cows. That gave us a thriving herd — six cows and a bull. I raised registered bulls for twelve years, and the girls had a part in the cattle as well. They were more like pets than wild animals, and a sale of one of the bulls brought $700 to $1,000, which meant quite a bit to us for buying feed for the other animals.

For the first three or four years I tended the animals with a shovel and a wheelbarrow. I was always busy, as removing manure and bringing in bedding was done by hand. One day Anita's mom surprised me with a sixteen-horsepower garden tractor with a wagon to haul manure and hay. I still did a lot of work by hand, but this went a long way to streamlining my operation. Yes, I drove a tractor blind. This was accomplished as I had learned the property so long ago with Heidi leading me by the hand. I used the shade from the trees to tell were I was. Going over the mounds, just like with my feet, I could feel with the tractor tires, although I never went fast. The tractor also had a mower attachment so I could easily mow out weeds and tall grass.

Our farm was making some money, so Anita and I began to save for emergency veterinary care. We also wanted a larger tractor with a bucket on the front so we wouldn't have to shovel anymore.

One day on my radio program I heard about an old Ford tractor with a hydraulic bucket for $1,200. I simply had to see it, so we called and made an appointment. It looked good to me — it needed some work, but nothing I couldn't do so we bought it and took it home. I couldn't drive this machine this by myself. Anita drove it sometimes, but she was gone a lot. So once again I enlisted my children. I would sit on the tractor with one of them in my lap and they would tell me which way to steer. Then I would operate the bucket. To their delight, they got to raise the bucket up, then we would take it to the pile and they would get to push the button to dump the manure. If we made a mistake we would just back up, pick it up again and put it where it needed to go. Yes, we had accidents with this tractor, but no one was ever hurt — we simply knocked the barn door off. If we got too close on the way in or out and hit the door we would have to stop and put the barn door back on. This happened three times in one week before I learned how to make the turn.

The kids were good to help me, and we had a lot of good times. I did a lot of things during those years, most of it with my family. Anita would help me, too — she is still a darn good mechanic. She knows the sizes of wrenches and so do both my children. There was always someone in the family available to help me. I used to come into the house and say "Hey, I need to borrow an eyeball." This was a common expression. It meant I needed someone to come out and see something or describe something to me.

They knew I depended on them for these descriptions. Any one of them could describe something in such vivid detail you could paint a picture by what they said. They have gotten to be experts over the years. Heidi was the manager of the women's clothing department at Wal-Mart, and when blind women came in to buy clothes Heidi always helped them. When they complimented her on how descriptive she was Heidi would explain that her dad had been blind for thirty years.

After several years of no contact I received a call from the Veterans Administration telling me of yet another VIST coordinator. His name was Richard Henderson, and he wanted me to come to Portland for a physical. In Portland I got the same answer: they couldn't see in and I couldn't see out, and "We don't think there is anything we can do." Richard Henderson was a blinded Veteran also, and he was going to do something for blind veterans. I felt we had the right man in the position, as no one since Mr. Mosiani had tried to do anything for me. On the way home I felt a little down, but I still had hope that someday there would be something they could do. At a family dinner I told everyone not to give up. I was still young, and someday they would be able to do something. We can't ever give up, I told my family.

One day one of my daughters brought a poster home. It was a picture of a stork with a frog in its mouth. The frog's head is in the stork's mouth but its arms are wrapped around the stork's neck, holding it so the stork can't swallow him. The caption is "Don't ever give up." How fitting, I thought. With everything I had been through this was the perfect motto for me.

When Heidi started high school one of the courses she chose was FFA, Future Farmers of America. She had always loved the farm and really wanted to excel at this. When I met her instructor, Gene Kantola, on parent-teacher night we discovered we had a lot in common with our farm backgrounds. My offer to help him with FFA began a six-year relationship with Mr. Kantola and the high school kids. Both of our daughters were involved in FFA, Heidi continuing with her hogs and Holly with her registered Shorthorn cattle. Both served as president of the club and were the only two students to attend the national FFA convention in Kansas City. Anita and I were both elected honorary members and became chapter farmers for the North Valley FFA, for our work with the students.

In 1985 Mr. Henderson called with some encouraging news. The VA was changing the way it rated hearing disabilities, which he believed would result in more compensation for my hearing loss. I was to go to Portland for a physical, another eye exam and a hearing test. My records showed that I had a hearing loss, and I had had an unsuccessful operation in Palo Alto when I was in blind school. Mr. Henderson thought this could be a huge thing — it could mean a lot of money.

In Portland, once again there was nothing they could do for my eyes, and the results of the hearing test were to be mailed to me later. On the way home I told Anita I felt disappointed. I thought after seventeen years there would be some help for me. Anita told me I couldn't give up — eventually they would come up with something.

When the letter from the Veterans Administration came it said I had acute tinnitus and perforated eardrums, with no compensation. I couldn't believe it. I had been unable to hear clearly in my left ear for seventeen years, and they said I didn't have hearing loss. It was just something else they didn't want to help me with.

Shortly after this we began to hear about laser surgery for eyes. I thought maybe the VA was behind the times, so I made an appointment with a doctor in Medford to ask about the new eye surgery. I told the doctor about my accident, and he asked if I was being seen by the Veterans Administration. Yes, I said, but they never offered laser surgery and I thought there might be some hope with this new technology. After no more than a four-second look in my eye he said, "I don't know how to tell you this, but you are hopelessly blind. Your eye is so vascularized there can never be a cornea transplant or anything else done for your sight and it would be criminal if I told you anything different."

Although I knew my eye had been badly damaged, his words stung. Driving home, Anita and I agreed that someday, someone would be able to help me. Maybe someday, I said, they'll be able to transplant an eye. There had to be something. I was still reasonably young.

I went back to the farm and enjoyed my life. Being blind wasn't as bad as some other things. I really felt easy with being blind now. The kids in 4-H and FFA had always accepted me, and I got along with people. I could farm very well and I had freedom of movement. This was better than a lot of ways other people lived their lives.

As the years went on I realized my daughters were not little girls anymore. They were growing into young women. Anita and I attended all of our children's activities — FFA meetings and all their athletic events. We never missed a game. We supported our kids as far as we could, so they would turn out to be decent people and good parents.

As Heidi grew closer to graduation in 1986 we began to downsize the hog operation. At our high point we had two boars, a Berkshire and a registered Duroc, and ten sows, registered Berkshire and Duroc as well as grade sows. We also had our own feed making system, but for the last three years, even with grinding our own feed we barely broke even. There was very little profit, but we had a good time and Heidi was able to show the animals at the state fair and with FFA. It was a learning opportunity that she never will forget. Of course the fringe benefits were that we got the freshest bacon, ham, and pork loins at basically no cost.

My children were growing up and flexing their wings and wanting to leave the nest. Heidi had enough credits to graduate from high school early, so while she waited to return for the graduation ceremony she took a job in my cousin's clothing store. She was a natural at clothing sales and soon was offered a job as assistant manager of a clothing store in Medford, twenty-five miles away, so she was out on her own. Holly was interested in becoming a travel agent, which told me that she, too, didn't want to stay on the farm. I wanted my daughters to live their lives as they saw fit. I gave them a background and a foundation using farming, and they would never forget that. Above all, they had learned how to put in a hard day's work without complaining — just enjoy it and be the best at it.

I felt it was all coming to a close, so I began to downsize the cattle as well as the hogs. With my daughters growing up and leaving home my interest in the farm began to diminish. The job was no longer fun — it became work, and the rewards were no longer there. Each trip to the barn became silent and haunting without the sound of my children. Just dead silence. I still made hay, but gave it to the hay man to take it off the field. We didn't need a big garden for the two of us, and Anita and I just rattled around the big, four-bedroom house. There was no reason to keep the farm, and it was a huge amount of work. The maintenance alone was very time-consuming. We had never really had a summer vacation or been able to travel because of the farm. We always had the animals, and we couldn't leave when we had animals that depended on us. For me, personally, I felt I needed a new outlook on life. I needed a reason to get out of bed.

I approached Anita with the idea of selling the farm and buying a place that had something I could do. She agreed that it was too much work and also, she felt it was time for her mother to live with us. Madge was eighty-five and was beginning to have memory lapses, occasionally leaving things cooking on the stove. I loved Anita's mother more than my own. She had been so good to me and always had a smile on her face. Anita's mom had helped us tremendously over the years. She showed me what it meant to be a parent, and she was my number one supporter for over twenty years.

A real estate agent confirmed what I thought about our farm. Although farming was becoming a thing of the past our place had increased in value because of the river frontage. Someone would buy it to build a secluded house down on the river. It was a very pleasant spot, with wildflowers in bloom and a nice breeze from the river. It was my job to keep the place like a park, and I did. We put it up for sale and began to look for other property.

I wanted a bigger place, one with no neighbors. I had shared the fenceline with seventeen neighbors at the farm. I had complaints at times about the noise of the animals and it was a constant battle to get along with seventeen neighbors. I loved the woods, and I wanted to live in the woods and harvest the trees, kind of like a permanent camping trip.

We found a place with 160 acres in a little town called Murphy, a former mill town ten miles south of Grants Pass. It has a gas station, lumber yard, grocery store, post office and a couple of restaurants, and that's it — that's Murphy. It's the oldest town in the Applegate Valley, on the trail my ancestors took to Oregon so many years ago. The property had been logged in the early 1960s, but it had been done badly. The woods had slash, rotten trees and other abuse. But it would give me something to do, and the roads were already in. The landing where they loaded the logs was a beautiful home site, just gorgeous. It seems like you can see a hundred miles in spots — up the Applegate River, around to the California border, across a couple of mountain ranges and all the way to the other side of Grants Pass. It is simply lovely. We decided to make our home there.

The process moved quickly. Our home sold in August and we began working with a contractor on our new house. This was to be

Anita's dream home, the place we planned to live for the rest of our lives. In all our years at the old house we had painted and wallpapered, but it was still an old house. With all she had put up with over the years, Anita deserved a new house.

The contractor listened to our ideas about room layout and cabinets and came back with sets of building plans. From the oak cabinets to the tile roof — everything was there, just as we wanted them. Mel Sanford was the most congenial man I've ever known, and he went out of his way to build the home of our dreams.

While the house was under construction we faced one of the greatest tragedies of our life together: Madge was diagnosed with recurring breast cancer. The cancer had spread to her lungs and throat, and it was terminal. She had just a couple of months to live. While Anita took care of her, I would go to work on the new house, building my shop and getting the well in. We would bring Madge to her new home on the weekends to make sure it was being built the way she wanted. She tried to be positive, but we could tell she was hurting.

Both of our daughters had moved back to southern Oregon. Heidi had taken a management position with a clothing store in Portland, but the noise and crowds were not for her. She was a small town girl in a big city, so when her apartment lease was up she left her job and moved back to her hometown. She found a job and renewed the relationship with Jeff Stevens, her high school sweetheart.

Holly had moved to Florida for travel agent training but she, too, missed her home and moved back to this area. She had met a nice young man, Cole Wilson, and soon she came home with a ring on her finger.

"Daddy, Cole asked me to marry him."

"Well, what did you say?"

"I said yes, of course."

Holly asked if they could be married in the front yard. "I spent my whole life here," she said, "and I want to be married here." So Anita and I planned an old-fashioned farm wedding. We invited more than sixty people — kids Holly had gone to school with, her 4-H leaders and family friends. On May 27, 1989, Cole and Holly said their vows in our front yard and I got to fulfill my obligation and walk my daughter down the aisle.

Both Heidi and Holly were grief-stricken when they learned of their grandmother's illness. Heidi and Jeff were planning to be married and they wanted Madge to see their wedding, so they moved up the date. On October 20, 1990, Jeff and Heidi said their vows, and I finished my obligation and walked my daughter down the isle at the Redwood Country Church where she became Mrs. Jeff Stevens.

As our February moving day approached we called on friends for help. They knew of Madge's condition and readily agreed to help with the move. We moved into the house right on schedule, but Anita's mother was failing rapidly. We literally moved her in her bed into her new room so she could look out the window. By this time Madge was very sick, almost comatose. Sometimes she would only awaken once a day or every other day. Holly and Cole were expecting their first child, but it looked like Madge would not live to see her first great-grandchild. In less than a week we had to take her for nursing care for her final days.

That winter was a difficult time. The weather was bad, and Anita grieved for her mother. Madge had been a major part of our lives and we all felt the loss. I turned my attention to building a deck across the entire back of our house, overlooking Murphy and across to two majestic mountain ranges. I began planning a pond that I would build alongside the deck that I would stock with fish in hopes of teaching my grandson how to fish someday.

The first couple of years were spent burning stumps and creating a meadow below the house and putting in a small lawn and gravel around the house for fire control. This open space and the tile roof would protect the house in case of a ground-sweeping fire. Other than fire control, we didn't want to bring in bulldozers and make major changes to the property. We had neighbors here — the animals — and we wanted them to stay. This was their home, too, and we wanted to coexist with them.

Our favorite pastime was to go on long walks in the woods. No one else, just the two of us holding hands and walking down the trails. Anita would describe the flowers and plants at different times of the year

As my friends who worked in the woods came to visit I would have them go on walks or drives with me and ask them what I could do to this property to make it right and repair the cluttered mess so all the trees could grow. They all agreed that the old hardwood trees needed to come out. The young firs and other trees would become huge if the hardwood canopy was removed. Some of the older trees were three or four feet wide at the stump, and the lowest limbs were eighty or ninety feet above ground. In order to release this forest these old trees would have to be removed.

I started by having my friend Tom Keith clear some of the roads, shoving the manzanita back so we could get through with equipment and go to work. We had spent three years learning where the animals lived and where they came from, and I had made a plan for what I wanted to accomplish. I listened to a retired logger that I knew, and I purchased an old 1951 HD5 Alice Chalmers cat. I couldn't drive, but I called on Dave Bradd. He had been hurt in a logging accident and this was something for him to do. We worked every morning, with Dave running the cat and clearing the roads. Dave was a good logger. He knew his business and he really liked the forest. He would educate me on the woods and how to maintain them.

Dave would fall the trees and drag them to the landing and cut them up for me to make into firewood. We had huge piles of firewood — some was sold or traded, and Dave took some in exchange for his work. We had a grand time in our five years of working together. We only took off days when it was raining hard because we both loved the work. I was becoming a middle-aged man and I needed the exercise more than ever. I enjoyed the hard work and had a good feeling at the end of a day. I now had a hydraulic wood splitter instead of a wedge and maul. The amount of wood behind us at the end of the day was very refreshing. You could see your accomplishments at the end of the day.

Anita and I were now semi-retired. She was still bowling twice a week, and after I got back to the house from working we would go on long walks together. Anita would tell me how our improvements looked and how the trees were beginning to grow.

In 1995 I had Larry Brown, a logging contractor, do a log thinning on our property. This consisted of a cruise, an estimate of the board feet of lumber on our property, as well as thinning the larger trees so the stand would become uniform. Thinning a forest is much like thinning a garden. You have to take out the big plants or the smaller ones will not survive. In the process of removing the big trees the tracks from the cat would crush the pine cones and seeds into the ground so they would seed themselves and reforest the area. Larry explained that this would need to be done about every fifteen years to keep the forest healthy, which meant I would be able to log it again before I retired at the official age of sixty-five.

We did reasonably well with the first logging, removing twenty-nine truckloads of logs. There are a lot of a trees at ten inches in diameter, and with the rains they will grow well. Next time there will be four to five times as many trees to take out.

My first grandchild, Cameron Scott Wilson, was now almost two years old. Heidi was also expecting a child. We were to have a granddaughter, Shelby Lynn Stevens, on December 18, 1993. Anita and I delighted in our grandchildren.

At each visit Cameron wanted to go to the pond to see the fish. Cameron was a real experience, but he didn't know how to take me. He just couldn't understand that I could not see. Holly would hold her hands over his eyes and I would hold my hands over his eyes but when you took your hands away he could see again. Even when he was eight years old and I got my sight back he still couldn't understand I hadn't been able to see.

Our children visited us often and we got to see our grandchildren grow up much like we did our own children. We saw them virtually every week, both our children and grandchildren. We are still very close.

In 1992 I received a letter from the Army saying that I may have to go on Medicare. I promptly called Richard Henderson, my VIST coordinator, and again I was told not to worry. They would take care of me. I didn't need this Medicare stuff. I believed this and made a call to the insurance company that covered Army veterans. I told them about the letter and they said Well, if you are a 100% disabled veteran there is nothing for you to worry about. I didn't need this coverage. The letter also said I would be notified at a later date about my Army retirement.

Life went on as normal until 1995, when I hurt myself. My back was very painful and I was afraid I might also have kidney stones. I went to the doctor in Grants Pass where I had been seen on a fee basis by the VA since 1970. He examined me, gave me some pain pills and told me he no longer wanted to see me. The VA had made it too difficult for them to deal with and he couldn't see me anymore. He asked me either to go to the VA or find another physician.

I could not believe this; I was so humiliated. I had been seen at this clinic for over twenty-five years, and now they were telling me they didn't want me as a patient.

Now I had no medical care. I called the VA administrative office in Roseburg where they coordinated my veteran's benefits and asked for the name of a doctor in Grants Pass who would see me, and who would accept their pay schedule. They offered no help, and I couldn't find a doctor for four years. I had ruled out going to the VA hospital, as it was eight-five miles one way and over two mountain ranges. In the wintertime this trip is very dangerous.

In March 1998 Anita picked up the mail and called me in and said I had received an interesting letter from the Department of Defense. As she read the letter I could not believe what I was hearing. After all these years I had ten days to apply for Medicare because insurance coverage through the military would no longer be available after July.

I could barely understand the letter's legalese, so I made an appointment at the local Veterans office, where they confirmed that I needed to go to the Social Security office and apply for Medicare. Now were dealing with another bureaucracy. The Social Security office didn't know anything about a contract with Department of Defense. I spoke to several people at the Social Security office and never got the same story twice. One person said that if I didn't sign up by the end of the month I would be liable for penalties. Another told me I had to pay all the back years that I wasn't on Medicare, which was twenty-seven years of back payments plus a ten percent penalty for every year. What cost everyone else $45.50 per month was going to cost me $163 for listening to the people that the government had hired to help me. I was told also that you can only sign up for Medicare between January 1 and March 31 of each year, which I was not able to do.

The following January I again called the Social Security office to explain the situation. I talked to people whose age was less than the time I had been blind, and these young people were not considerate. One woman asked if I had this in writing. I didn't think I needed to defend myself with paperwork from people that I had served and lost my eyesight for some thirty years before. I realized I didn't have any special care coming, but the least they could do was to be civil. I then contacted the service organizations that I had belonged to for years. I learned they were aware of the situation but they didn't feel there was anything they could do. So I took the same path I had taken years before and wrote a letter about my medical care which I hand-delivered to my congressman, Greg Walden. Congressman Walden and his staff in Medford helped me get Medicare at the price I was supposed to pay — $45.50, like everyone else. They also found a doctor, Brian Tanczos, who would see me at the new clinic in Grants Pass.

I learned from organizations I belonged to and the congressman's office that more than 13,000 disabled veterans had received similar treatment. I can't imagine what the others went through. I know what I went through and it is very upsetting to know the people you served and lost your sight for could treat you this poorly. The way I was treated by the government since the 1980s was disgusting. The system is broken. I don't know how it will ever be fixed, but believe me, it is broken. This bureaucracy thrives on itself; they get all the money and the Veterans seem to get the short end of the stick. For example, the January/February 1999 issue of the blinded veterans bulletin reported that the Department of Veterans Affairs, as it is called now, has a budget of $44 billion and spends over $4 billion maintaining buildings they no longer use. Why doesn't someone stop this and give that $4 billion to the veterans who need it and deserve it? The next time you see a disabled veteran on the street asking for money, ask yourself what the VA has done to him or for him. Does he have to live on the street because some bureaucrat denied his claim? This and many other questions go through my mind constantly. I know how I was treated and I wonder how veterans who needed help more than I did were treated.

My last physical exam by a VA doctor had been in 1988. Once again they had looked into my eye and said they couldn't see in and I couldn't see out. There was no change, and after seeing the doctor in Medford I began to agree with them. I would always hold out a thread of hope that I would see again, but twenty years had gone by and I had spent half my life blind. It was becoming normal. Seeing was a distant memory. I now "saw" with my hands and I felt comfortable with that. I could do anything, with the exception of flying an airplane or driving a car, and I was not afraid to try anything.

The greatest compliment I ever received was from a woman on Anita's softball team. She put her arm around me and said "Heck, John isn't blind. He just doesn't see very well." To my family, I believe they thought I was as normal as anyone else. People don't think a blind person knows what is going on, but you can ask either of my daughters. They will tell you I always knew exactly what was going on. They could never pull the wool over my eyes.

By the time we had settled into our home in the woods and negotiated the government bureaucracy I had been blind for over thirty years, and I had learned to make my way in the world. The world sees and I had found my place in it as a blind person. I never had any special activities with other blind people. Instead, I tried to make my life in a seeing world. My wife Anita and I enjoy our home and walk our mountain and do as we please. I have my children and my grandchildren, and I can teach them about their roots in Oregon.

People often ask me why I say "I saw" something, instead of "it was shown to me." Blind people see things, we truly do. We don't use vision; we see through other people's sight or through our hands. It is common for blind people to use the expression "I saw," or "Look over there," as anyone else would say. It's the way we all communicate. A vivid imagination helps, too. When you talk to someone you begin to "put a face with the name." As the years go by you make a mental picture of what things look like. It makes life more bearable. It may be cartoon-like or realistic, but it happens. Since regaining my sight I have told many people that their face does not fit their voice. They laugh and say it's like talking to someone on the telephone and then meeting him or her for first time. It's a way we can all relate to this experience.

Part 2

Chapter 6

'I Think I Can Help You'

As 1999 began I was continuing the nine-month ordeal with Medicare. My health care was nonexistent, and everyone I talked to seemed to pass the buck. It was disheartening to have served my country and then to be treated so badly by all levels of government. I was one of 13,000 veterans dropped somewhere between military coverage and Medicare. The local Social Security office had no idea what I was talking about, and my letter to Champus Insurance went unanswered. Meanwhile, the March 31 deadline for enrolling in Medicare was quickly approaching.

Anita and I contacted a medical clinic that agreed to see me, a disabled veteran, and made an appointment with Dr. Brian J. Tanczos. I knew I had high blood pressure, I explained, and was taking medication for it, but I had not had any tests or lab work for four years. Dr. Tanczos ordered a blood work-up and made an appointment for me to return after the tests.

One evening a call came that would change my life forever. It didn't come from the government agencies that you would expect — the VA or Department of Defense or Social Security — but from my cousin's husband, whom I hadn't seen in thirty years. He wanted to tell me about a doctor from Eugene who was doing a seminar on the new eye surgeries. He thought maybe the new technology could help me. I told him I hadn't been to an eye doctor for years; they had all told me there was no hope. Still, he wanted to know how much I could see so he could ask about my situation. Three days later Don Williams called to report that the ophthalmologist, Dr. Scott Cherne, thought he could help me, although he didn't know how much. I was elated and cautiously hopeful.

Anita and I talked about what to expect. Maybe, after all these years, they might be able to help me.

"I think you're right," she said. "We may have to pay for it ourselves but I can't let a chance go by if they can make you see again." We called Dr. Cherne's office and made an appointment for May eleventh.

When the VA turned down Dr. Tanczos's request for blood work I began to feel I was losing the health care game. I had played by the rules all these years and I had a wallet full of medical cards that were no good. I knew it was beyond me, so I decided to see my congressman. I wrote and delivered a letter to Representative Greg Walden explaining my situation with Medicare and Social Security. His staff immediately went to work and got my lab tests approved and Medicare enrollment at the regular fee of $45.

The test results were not good. My blood pressure was high. I was a little overweight and I had diabetes and inherited high cholesterol. Dr. Tanczos said there would have to be some changes in my life or the results would not be good. I was in full agreement. It had been a long time since I had seen a physician and things had gotten away from me. We discussed treatment and he put me on a diet for diabetes, prescribed cholesterol medication and recommended that I work out on an exercise bicycle every day.

I had been a huge fan of George Foreman, the world heavyweight champion. One of the last things I remember seeing was the young George Foreman winning the gold medal at the Mexico City Olympics and waving the American flag with his gloved hand. I had followed his career and his inspiring comeback. If George can do it, I thought, so can I. My diet and bike riding routine were like training for a fight.

On May 11, the biggest day of my life, Anita and I drove to Eugene for the appointment. I was very nervous in the examining room but I had a feeling this was the help I had been looking for all these years. Soon there was a knock on the door and Dr. Cherne and his assistants came into the room. He made small talk and then said, "That is a serious case of road rash you've got." I told him it was from an explosion; silver nitrate had been blown into my skin. He became serious.

"Do you know that can all be taken off your skin?"

No, I said, I had no idea that was possible. Dr. Cherne took a seat in front of me and after looking at my eye for a few minutes he backed away from the slit lamp. "I think I can help you. I don't know how much, but I can make it better." I would need a corneal transplant and a lens transplant.

"Doctor," I said, "I have been told for thirty years that it was impossible to do a corneal transplant on my eye."

"I don't know who told you that," he said, "but I can do a corneal transplant and a lens transplant." I had always been told there were too many veins in my eye, that it wouldn't take. He took another look with the slit lamp.

"No, I only see two veins. I think it is totally possible for you to have a corneal transplant." Then he added those familiar words: "You can't see out and I can't see in." Dr. Cherne wanted me to see a retina specialist before the surgery. Dr. Timothy You was finishing his training at Harvard and would join the practice in August. I agreed to wait for an appointment.

"I'm in no hurry," I said. "I have one chance and I have been blind for over thirty years. What's a few months?" He took another measurement and concluded, "I see no reason why I can't do the corneal transplant."

Anita and I made the appointment for August third, some four months away, and left the office in disbelief. There was finally hope. This was the most positive statement in over twenty-five years, but I warned her that we had to wait for Dr. You's verdict, and we had to be prepared for the worst. I didn't want anyone in the family to get their hopes up in case the surgery could not be done.

The waiting time literally crawled by. I needed to get the wood supply in and finish all the summer projects. Anita and I both pitched in on things that needed to be done before winter. I didn't know how long the recovery would be if I did have surgery.

At my check-up with Dr. Tanczos I told him about the hope of being able to see again. He was happy for me, but there was a problem. My blood sugar and cholesterol were still too high. "You are doing well," he said, "but you need to do more. Right now I couldn't recommend a corneal transplant. Your blood sugar wouldn't let you heal well." He wanted me to see a dietitian. "Your exercise is good and the weight is coming off, but I think you can do better."

I met with the dietitian, even though I had lost twenty pounds and thought I was starving. She gave me some pointers and I began to work harder at my diet and exercise. I knew this was the fight of my life, and I had to win. George Foreman was always in my thoughts. I knew he had to train hard to beat Michael Moore, many years his junior. For a forty-eight-year-old man to be able to go three minutes a round for twelve rounds and compete with younger men was simply unbelievable, but it could be done and I had to do it too.

Finally the day came for my appointment with the retina specialist. This was the day of destiny, when I would learn whether I could have the operation. Dr. Timothy You had already discussed my case with Dr. Cherne. I was to have a test that gives an ultrasound image of the entire eyeball, showing a detached retina or other problems. Dr. You set the machine and began to move the wand around on my eye, asking me to move my eye to the right, left, up, down, then straight ahead. Soon he reached over and shut off the machine and stepped back. His words still echo in my ears.

"I don't see any reason you can't have the operation," he said. "I think it's a go. If anything is there it is minor, and I can fix it."

"Now it's time to get excited!" I jumped out of the chair and hugged Dr. You, then Anita. The surgery was set for August 31, just twenty-eight days away.

Anita and I were elated. Anything would be an improvement over just seeing light and dark and very large objects. After all these years it was finally my turn. It was the happiest I had been since the birth of my children.

I called Heidi and Holly with the good news. As we began to notify our friends everyone asked how much I was going to be able to see. I had no answers and I, too, was curious about the operation. A week before the surgery I felt I had to talk to the doctors. I wanted to know what they were going to do. I wasn't apprehensive, but I was nervous and my emotions were in a dither. All I knew was that I was having eye surgery and with God's help I would see again.

Dr. Cherne explained that Dr. You would begin. He would remove the lens in my eye and if there was any retina damage he would repair it. Then Dr. Cherne would put in the new lens and do the corneal transplant. I was sure everything was going to be fine, I said. I just wished it could happen sooner.

"Let me see what I can do." That evening Dr. Cherne called to say he had rescheduled the surgery for August 27 at two o'clock. I was ready and 100 percent positive it would be successful. I could not think of anything else.

I had been blind for more than 19,000 days and nights. I used to lie in bed and pray for the day that was coming, for a chance to see and especially to see my wife and children. Every blind person ends each day with the same thoughts: just a glimmer of light, a hope for the future that they might give up the cloak of darkness and be given a new beginning. Now it was my turn. I had no idea why, but I sincerely believe it was divine intervention that got me out of Veterans Affairs and onto Medicare to be seen by competent doctors, and then the call from my cousin. It couldn't be coincidence. I am not a religious man, nor do I claim to be. But I have always led my life in a truthful and honorable manner, and I have tried to be the person everyone wants to be as a father and as a mentor for the kids in 4-H and FFA. I always tried to teach not only farming but also lessons in life — how to overcome handicaps and shortcomings and make the best of a bad situation.

I do believe in a supreme being that is in our lives whether we know it or not. It is said that we have a merciful God who will not give us more that we can stand. Sometimes I thought He had the wrong man when He did all this to me, but now I was sure that things were going to be made right. And just as surely, I believe He has more for me to do after the wondrous experience of having my sight restored.

At last the day arrived, and after a restless night the alarm finally rang at five. I swung my legs out of bed and began to get ready for the three-hour journey from Murphy to Eugene. An hour later we met Heidi and Holly and began the caravan to the Clear Vision Institute in Eugene. I was not afraid. I knew this would be the last day I would be blind.

At ten o'clock I was escorted to a room where Dr. Scott Cherne, the doctor that was going to do the cornea transplant, and Dr. Timothy You, the retina specialist, would examine me. First Dr. Cherne measured my eye and thickness, the cornea size and length, with an instrument that measures the distance from the cornea to the lens and from the lens to the retina. Dr. Cherne told me we had a plus 5 cornea, the best to be implanted in my eye. Then it was Dr. You's turn: one last try to see into my eye through the terribly stained and missile-filled cornea. After all medical procedures were finished Dr. You, Anita, my wife of thirty-one years, and I said a prayer for guidance from our maker.

Back in the waiting room the office staff wished me well. They knew it was a go. While I was being examined the plus 5 cornea from an unknown donor had arrived at the airport and was being couriered to the hospital. Anita and I drove the three or four blocks to Saint Anne's Hospital where we nervously filled out insurance forms and signed permission papers for the operation.

In the pre-op area the nurses started an IV and gave me a light sedative. Finally the time came and I kissed my wife and daughters as I was wheeled to the operating room. As we pushed through the door of the operating room they asked me to slide onto the operating table. As they placed my arm in an automatic blood pressure cuff I can remember thinking, It is about to start, and that is the last thing I remember.

I woke up in the recovery room hearing a nurse telling me to breathe deeply and cough. I tried, but I wasn't doing well. She asked me to roll over onto my side, which I could not do. I couldn't move my arms; they felt paralyzed and I began to worry. She got the anesthesiologist, who began to rub my arms. As the circulation came back the nurse had me cough and breathe, and gradually I came out of the fog. I had had a bad reaction to the anesthesia, I guess. Instantly I became violently ill and was given medicine for the nausea. As the vomiting subsided, I was able to move my arms a bit, and they decided I could be moved into a room, where an angel of mercy began to take care of me through the night. I don't know her name but she had to have a halo over her head. I was in awful shape. My eye felt like someone had taken it out and dropped it on the floor, stepped on it and then put it back. I could tell there was swelling, and she put ice on my eye to relieve it. She gave me pain medication and I slept until about midnight, when I woke up in intense pain. I pushed the call button and she was there almost instantly, and she came back to check about every fifteen minutes during the rest of the night. Finally morning came and I was given a breakfast of oatmeal and juice. I ate greedily because I had had nothing to eat the previous day. Thankfully the nausea had subsided and let this stay on my stomach.

Anita came into the room alone. She wanted to tell me that, after more than four hours of surgery the doctors had come into the waiting area and told my family that, truthfully, they didn't know if I would be able to see anything. Maybe tunnel vision at best, which would be like looking down a pipe. They had dug a piece of wood out of my eye that had been there for thirty-one years, and there was a little more retina damage than Dr. You had expected, but he had repaired it. Dr. Cherne had placed the lens in my eye and they had done the corneal transplant, but they didn't know how well it would work. I had to stay positive, I told Anita. I couldn't believe I went through all this for nothing.

Later that morning Dr. You would remove the bandages and see the results. As the time drew near Anita and I and our two daughters, one on each side of me, left the hospital and drove to the office. Dr. You arrived and unlocked the door; it was Saturday and no one was there. He ushered us in and told us about the surgery and about removing the small piece of wood from my eye.

He said there are no records in any medical book or any reason why my eye was there. He said I should have lost my eye many years ago from infection from the wood. My daughters and Anita grew concerned as Dr. You said, "Well, let's take off the bandage and see what we did."

He began to remove the bandage and I remember thinking, Please God, let it work. As the bandage came away, first in the upper right corner of my vision, I began to see an area of light. I could see this before so I knew I would still have light perception. I was struggling to process the information through my drugged state from the pain medication. As the bandage was lowered I could see more light, and finally it was off. Instantly I saw a blast of light similar to a film image of an atomic blast — a little twinkle of light, then a painfully bright blast. As this began to subside everything was blurry but I could see Dr. You's arm and the bandage. The first thing I saw was the beautiful gold watch he wore. I looked around, and I could see blurry objects but I didn't know what they were. I held my hand about six inches in front of my face and I could see my fingers. I held my hand to the side, because they had said I would have no peripheral vision, but I wiggled my fingers farther and farther away, and at the fullest extension of my left arm I could still see my fingers.

When I told Dr. You I could see my fingers moving and I did have peripheral vision he looked at Anita. "I want you to know this is a miracle." This immensely talented young doctor had performed the surgery of his life and repaired my retina so that I had vision I had only dreamed about in the past. It was blurry but I knew it would get better. We were already at 1,000 percent. Dr. You gave me a package with a pair of dark sunglasses and medicine, and he gave Anita instructions for the eye drops and cream. Before releasing me he asked if I wanted to know about the donor. Yes, I told him, absolutely. I felt obligated to thank the family. When Dr. You told me that it had been a thirty-year-old man who had died in an accident, the reality hit. The day before I had been so happy about receiving a cornea, but I immediately felt great sorrow. Because this young hero had unselfishly given his organs I, at age fifty-one, had received the gift of sight. This young man was almost the same age as my own daughters. He could have been my son. Looking around the office I could make out chairs and desks and I could see my children. I could see the color of their hair and the color of clothing they were wearing. It was blurry and somewhat distorted but by God, I could see them. Before we left Dr. You again said a prayer with us for healing, and I felt sure it would be answered.

I was tired and hungry, and ready to go home. As Anita drove I looked out the window. I could see trees; I couldn't tell what kind, but I could make out trunks and limbs. I could see street signs coming and then, when we approached, they would swoosh by at lightning speed. I began to feel nausea again, probably from the surgery, I thought. I closed my eyes and Anita asked how I was doing. I had been quiet for some time after the emotional morning, thinking of the young man who had donated his cornea to me.

It was nearing lunchtime, so we decided to stop at a Dairy Queen in Sutherlin for a hamburger and fries. We pulled in and Anita came around the car to get me. By habit I took my folding cane and put it in my pocket. I needed to use the restroom, so I walked in and took off the dark glasses. I stood there for a moment and I could see a door. I took out my cane and extended it to the full length of fifty-four inches, then pushed the door open. I could see there was no light inside. I knew that people don't like walking into a dark room and turning on a light and finding someone there. It ranges from shock, to horror, fear, and anger. I reached inside and switched on the light in the small bathroom. Immediately I could see the sink with a mirror above it and a paper towel rack. To the right was the toilet and urinal. I knew things in my life had changed, and I reached down and collapsed my cane and put it back in my pocket. I used the urinal, then walked over to the sink and washed my hands. It was so easy compared to the fumbling mess it had been for the past thirty-one years. It was unbelievable that something so simple could have such an effect. Achieving basic sanitation in a bathroom is very difficult for a blind person. The soap is not where it should be, and the paper towel holder is sometimes across the room. Then find a place to put the used paper towel. It is almost like someone is playing a cruel joke on you, just trying to see how difficult they can make it.

Back in the restaurant Anita took me to a table and went to get our order. Things were blurry, but I could see the food in front of me. I took the hamburger and looked at the colorful wrapper. Thirty-one years ago hamburgers were wrapped in plain white paper, but this box was very attractive. I reached for the iced tea, and as it moved I could see the ice in the top of the glass, shimmering and floating like diamonds.

"That is unbelievable," Anita said.

"This whole day has been that way," I told her.

As we reached Grants Pass I asked Anita to drive slowly so I could look at my hometown. I hadn't seen it since my trip to Fort Lawton in 1968. Everything was blurry but I could see trees and some of the buildings. It didn't make a lot of sense; everything moved too fast. If I turned my head things would move at lightning speed, like the fast-forward on a VCR, or the way Charlie Chaplain walked in the old movies.

We drove through town and crossed the Rogue River. I remembered the bridge from when I was a kid. It still looked the same, with the two rainbow arches. We headed south on Highway 238, and as we came into Murphy Anita pointed out the Applegate River and the bridge we could see from our home. She pointed out the store and restaurant, but everything was too blurry to see. As we approached our home I asked Anita to go really slow up the driveway so I could try to see everything. I could make out the trees on our property. I could see the bright green on the treetops and the vivid shadows under them, but the images were one-dimensional and without perspective. Everything seemed flat, but at different distances. As we came closer to the house I felt I knew where I was, but it was not as I had expected. There was a nice blue house with a blue and gray roof and white trim around the windows, the colors I had selected. Anita parked the car in the garage and I got out. I could see the shelves that my son-in-law, Jeff, and I had built. They were blurry and badly out of focus but I knew what they were. Our freezer was there and the bin I kept full of wood.

As we entered the house it was like walking into someone else's home. I stopped for a moment and looked around. The light sources were where they used to be and so was the furniture, but the house didn't look the way I had pictured it in my mind. I had run my hands over everything but it is hard to remember colors like green and mauve. I complimented Anita on the lovely job she had done decorating our home and slowly made my way to the dining room table. It felt like I was standing still and everything else was moving. Everything was so different; it was hard to deal with. I felt like I needed to close my eyes and go back but I knew I couldn't do that. I would never be satisfied to go back. I sat down at the table and held onto it. I looked around and noticed the pictures on the wall and the saw blade that I had had painted for Anita's birthday three years before. It has a picture of Mount Shasta with a lake below it, with the mountain reflected in the lake and trees around the edge. I could see the green of the trees but the mountain looked like a white blob. The chair I always sat in didn't look right; it was a beautiful Kelly green. The wood stove was brown, but in my mind's eye it had been black although I knew Anita had chosen a brown stove when we built the house. Our loveseat was a multitude of colors — I couldn't believe all the colors in it. I moved down the hall that led to our bedroom. At the corner, right where it was supposed to be, was the grandfather clock I had given Anita for our twentieth wedding anniversary. I had never seen it. I touched it and felt the walnut wood and the beveled doors. I couldn't see the bevel but I could feel it with my hands. Now the combination of sight and feel were taking hold. Somehow I didn't trust what I was seeing — it was too soon, so I touched things to make sure my brain wasn't deceiving me. I could see color, but things didn't look as I had remembered or pictured them. For several days I kept reaching out and touching things. Simple things like knives, forks, and tools in my shop — I had to touch them to believe what I was seeing. I needed to rest, I told Anita. I was tired, and everything was overwhelming, just too much to comprehend.

Anita was making spaghetti for dinner. I felt so weak, I thought some quick energy food would help. A few hours later she came in and said it was time to get up, dinner would be ready soon. I felt much better, and the nausea was gone. I slowly opened my eye and it was all there. I could still see, and I thanked God for not taking my sight away while I slept.

I sat down at the table and looked around my house again. I watched Anita cooking dinner, and as blurry as she was, I told her, if people could see what I see now they would think they were blind. But I thought I was the luckiest man in the world. I looked out at the redwood deck that I had built nearly ten years before, then I opened the sliding glass door and walked out to the picnic table and sat down. Again I had to hold on. Then I realized it wasn't the medicine that was making me sick, it was motion sickness. The feeling that my brain was sending was that I was staying still and everything else was moving, much like being on a rocking ship. This feeling would begin to ease, but it did not end for three weeks. As I walked around on the deck and then went back inside it felt strange not to use a cane or my usual landmarks to move around. Things seemed familiar but yet so unfamiliar.

Anita was putting dinner on the table when I went back inside. She set down a plate and I looked at this thing they call spaghetti. It was the first time I had seen it in thirty-one years, and it looked revolting: white noodles and red sauce. I fought the wave of nausea hitting me and thought, I have to eat this after Anita worked so hard to make it to please me. I ate very slowly and Anita asked me what was wrong.

"You have no idea how bad this looks, Anita." She laughed and said, "I've made it the same way for thirty-one years."

"No, it tastes fine," I said. "It just has an awful appearance."

That evening Anita and I watched TV. It was hard for me to watch the screen; everything moved so fast and seemed to jump up and down and side to side. It took some time to slow down to the right speed, but it fascinated me. After looking at a dark screen and hearing voices for thirty-one years I realized there were some very entertaining things on TV. I had preferred to read talking books to watching TV. I enjoyed watching some sporting events and some shows with my family, but television is for the sighted person. Blind people don't get much out of it.

That evening the anesthesiologist called to ask how I felt. I was fine, I said. I had full motion in my arms but was still having waves of nausea. He said that sometimes happens when you have a bad reaction to the medicine, but it should go away in three or four days.

By nine o'clock I had had enough. It was time for bed. It felt so strange to look over and see my wife undressing and putting on her nightclothes. I had missed so much all those years. We got into bed and I hugged Anita and told her things were going to get better and better. I had no idea where the end would be, but I had a feeling that I was going to get more of my vision back than we had thought.

During the night I woke in a panic. My heart was racing as I ran into the bathroom and turned on the light. I could still see. I went back to the bedroom and grabbed my Braille watch. It was two-thirty so I got back into bed, but there was no going back to sleep, and every so often I got up to make sure I could still see. I don't know why. I guess I thought if I went to sleep this would all be taken away from me. When dawn came I went into the living room to wait for Anita to get up. I told her about my long night. I didn't know if this was normal or not, because everything that was normal was changed.

After breakfast and my exercise routine I showered and came out into the living room. I began to make the rounds of the pictures on the walls. I looked at Mount Shasta and a picture that we inherited from Anita's mother of the Grand Tetons. I could see the meadows and mountains, some pine trees and yellow brush and a lake in the center of the painting. I went to look at the face of the grandfather clock I had given Anita. It seemed a little clearer. Outside, things looked the same. After lunch I again needed to rest. Anita asked if there was anywhere I wanted to go, or anything I wanted to see, but I knew it would be a day or two before I felt well enough to go out. All the familiar things that I had known were gone. Everything was new and it was totally overwhelming. I felt more comfortable at home.

My children had called every day and my grandson Cameron had called to ask, "Grandpa, what can you see today?" After another restless night I told Anita I wanted to go to Wal-Mart to see Heidi and look around. On the way into town I pictured things the way I "saw" them when I was blind. There was no comparison. I had had no idea what I was seeing. There were mountains where I thought there were farms, and vice versa. I could see street signs and posts. I couldn't see what was written on them, but I could see their shapes. I could see the colors of cars going by. They seemed to approach very slowly, but when they got close they would flash by in a startling motion. Anita parked the car and as we walked toward the store I began to look at the automobiles. What cars looked like took me aback. They all had a sleek look, with rounded fronts like bullets. They reminded me of futuristic movies of what life would be like in the twenty-first century. The cars looked just like that. It was like I had seen them before, back when I could see.

As we walked into the store I was amazed. There were so many things on the shelves; I had never seen such a selection of stuff in my life. I understand now how immigrants feel when they come to this country and see all these things for the first time. It is overwhelming. The "land of plenty" has so much to choose from and so many varieties of each thing. We walked around the store and then to the women's clothing department where my daughter Heidi was the manager. I told her this was my first trip into town and I was in immigrant mode. She was brought to tears over what I could see. Of course all the employees were aware of my operation and were asking questions and congratulating me. It was overwhelming that so many people cared, but I was soon ready to go home. I had seen enough, and I wanted the solitude of my house and familiar things.

The trip had set off the motion sickness again and I was nauseated. When we returned home I went to take a nap. When I got up I walked around the house and checked to see if my vision had changed while I slept. It changed daily at this point. As we ate dinner I looked at Anita and I could see her face — her brown eyes and her graying black hair. She was the spitting image of her mother nearly thirty-two years ago. Anita could tell I was looking at her. She knew I was seeing her with different eyes than I had this morning. I could hardly wait to see my children.

After dinner I helped Anita clear the table, then we went to watch TV together. I was trying to figure out what to say to my lovely wife. I knew I had to say something and it had to be special. The next morning I looked at her. "You know," I said, "last night and this morning I can see you and it is pretty doggone clear. I can't see the pupils in your eyes but I can see that they are brown, and I can see your lovely gray-streaked hair. You look so much like your mother thirty-one years ago it is really unbelievable."

"Anita," I said, "I want you to know that the years have been very kind to you." She smiled and asked me if I had looked at myself yet. No, I told her, I really don't have the guts. As I did my exercise I wondered, if I could see Anita, what did I look like? In my mind's eye I looked like the twenty-year-old man that I remembered — young and full of life with a lot of dreams for the future. I knew that thirty-one years had to do something to you, I knew I had been through an explosion, and I knew my hair was gray. I had been told that. I exercised as usual, then went into the bathroom. I leaned over the sink, about fifteen or sixteen inches from the mirror, and there was my dad looking back at me in the mirror, just as plain as could be. He had black paint all over his face.

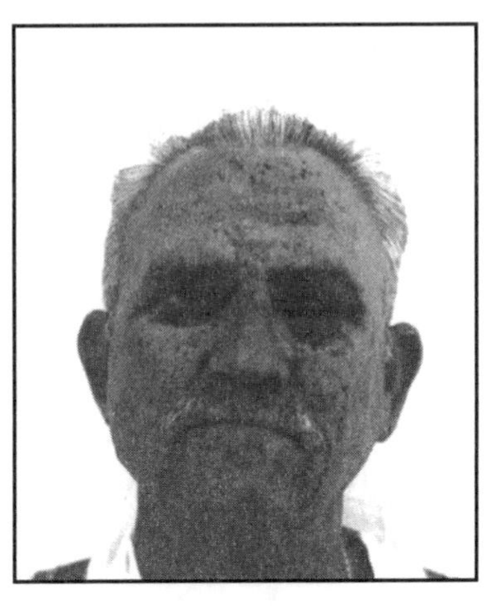

I remembered myself as I looked before the explosion. Nearly thirty-one years later I was shocked to see the old man looking back at me from the mirror.

After showering I took another look at myself. It was unbelievable what the years had done. I had become an old man, and my face was scarred and tattooed. I was embarrassed. I thought, What have you done to the people you love most? All these years no one had ever told me what I looked like. Dr. Wheatley had said I was freckled, but I wasn't freckled. My eyes were circled in black and my forehead looked like someone had shaken a black paintbrush against it. And this was after all the plastic surgery I had endured. I felt depressed.

I had been agonizing about the young man who had died, whose cornea I had received. I had felt the elation of seeing my wife again, and soon I would get to see my children. There was no doubt that my vision was getting better each day. Things were clearing, becoming less distorted. Each day I could see more detail in the pictures in our house. One pine tree was actually two trees growing close together. The yellow brush was turning into quaking aspen in fall color and the mountain was actually four peaks. In the kitchen I could see the bevel in the cupboard doors from six to eight feet away. Things were beginning to take shape. On the front of the refrigerator was the poster of the stork swallowing the frog. The frog was gripping the stork's neck so it couldn't swallow him. Under the picture was the caption, "Never ever give up." How fitting, I thought. This poster had been there for twenty years, and I had never given up. Things were getting clearer and I was going to see things I never thought possible.

That afternoon I stepped outside and walked to the end of the deck. I looked over the edge and felt the nausea hit, as if I was standing still and the deck was moving under me. I held on and looked down. There, on the ground below, was a butterfly. Its wings were orange with black trim; in the center was a blue circle with a white dot, similar to a deer's eye, or "buckeye," as we called it. I was overcome with emotion as I watched it flutter toward me. I thought of the thirty-one years that I had seen nothing. I couldn't take my eyes off this beautiful creature, and it didn't seem to want to leave, fluttering around within my view for the longest time. I stood there, tears running down my cheeks and off my chin in a steady stream. I watched the butterfly and silently wept until it finally disappeared. I felt relief after such an emotional outpouring, and I wiped my face and thanked God.

Chapter 7

How to Say Thank-You for a Miracle

The next morning Anita and I were due in Eugene for a follow-up appointment with Dr. You. The corneal transplant was doing fine, he said, the pressure was in the normal range, and the retina was "like a dike — holding in the good and keeping out the bad." He was happy with the surgery. Then he got my file and read us the pathologist's report on the piece of wood that had been in my eye all those years.

"This is a miracle," Dr. You said again. Already my vision was beyond their wildest dreams, and he thought there was a chance it would continue to improve. He asked what I had been doing and what I was able to see. I described how things were distorted and then became clearer. I told him how overwhelming it had been to watch the butterfly. Then he told me the results of the vision test. I could see the big E on the chart; my vision was at 20/200. I was finally able to see an eye chart, to see more than just light and dark. And now I had a number that people would understand when they asked how well I could see. Dr. You assured me that I was already better than he had expected, and he was certain this was a miracle in the making. He asked if I wanted the address of the Lions Eye Bank so I could write and thank the family of the donor. Yes, I told him, absolutely. I felt very sad about the man who lost his life. We said a prayer together for my continued healing. I was going to have useful vision, I just didn't know how much.

As we drove south on Interstate 5 I paid more attention to signs and scenery. I could tell the differences in shape and color although I could not read the signs. As we got closer to home the anticipation of the barbecue on Sunday began to weigh on my mind. What was I going to say to my children when I saw them for the first time?

I saw my daughters, Holly (left) and Heidi, for the first time on September 5, 1999.

That night I hugged Anita and told her how happy I was that Dr. You had thought the treatment was going to be successful. Anita was as happy as I have ever seen her. This had been an ordeal for her, also, and a heavy burden had been lifted from her shoulders. I tried to be self-sufficient, but still, I depended on her for a lot of things. Again that night I awoke at two o'clock, terrified that I couldn't see. I ran into the bathroom and turned on the light as I had done so many times before and yes, I could still see. I had no idea why, but this tormented me. I went back to bed and lay there wide-awake, thinking of the young man who had lost his life and his family. I needed to thank them. I got up and went into the living room and found a pencil and paper. This was my first attempt to write a letter by myself in thirty-one years. I placed the pencil between my index and middle finger, for I had no thumb to hold it. I began to write in large, block-print letters, sloppy at first, but I got better with practice. It was very difficult, but as the sun came up I had a letter — a wonderful letter, I thought. I had rewritten it several times to get the words just right. After Anita had her morning coffee I asked her to read the letter, as I was having a rough time with it. When she finished she wiped tears from her eyes.

"You've done a good job."

For three and a half hours in the middle of the night I had thought and written about what this family had lost and all I had gained from this loss. Writing that letter finally eased the grief that had been lingering in the shadows.

Every day I made my rounds, looking at the cabinets and pictures to see if anything was different. Things improved daily, even hourly. I didn't know if it was my eyesight or my brain finally being able to process what I was seeing. The next morning I sat up and watched the sunrise. September 5, 1999, the day I had waited for my entire life. So many nights I had prayed to God to let me see my children before I died, and now the day had come. I was going to see my two daughters.

As we drove to Holly's house things looked a lot clearer out the window. I had developed double vision so I sometimes had trouble distinguishing things, but the motion sickness had gotten better. I could ride in a car and keep my eyes open. If the nausea did come it was less severe. When we arrived at Holly's house a little eight-year-old boy came running out.

"Hi, Grandpa, I'm Cameron. Can you see me?" I bent over and looked into his beautiful face.

"Yes, I can see you, Cameron." He didn't look like Anita so I guessed that he looked like Cole, his dad.

I walked to the back deck with Anita and saw two young women standing in the sunlight. I approached slowly, trying to keep myself together, as I saw Anita thirty-one years before, in my older daughter, Heidi. To my left was Holly, a young woman with my eyes as I remember them so many years ago. The rest of her face looked like Anita's. They were both taller than Anita, with beautiful dark hair, big brown eyes and bright, perfect smiles. I had thought of a lot of things to say but at this moment the words would not come. I simply hugged them and wept with gratitude. After a few moments Holly stepped back.

"Well, Dad, what kind of job do you think you did?"

"With what?"

"With us," she said. "What do we look like? We've waited all these years."

"You both look like your mother," I said. "It is truly unbelievable how much Heidi looks like her mother."

After lunch I watched my grandson playing and heard all about his soccer league that was starting soon. After all the sporting events that I attended and listened to over the years, at last I could watch Cameron play.

As much I enjoyed and appreciated the day, I was haunted by something that took me some time to understand. The people in my life were strangers, even my own wife and children. When I saw people I had known for twenty years, the voice didn't fit the face. It wasn't the face I had imagined all those years. It was a difficult thing to deal with, and I felt lonely. I was surrounded by family and friends, but no one looked right; they were all strangers. When I left our house everything was so overwhelming I could only take it for an hour or two. Then I had to retreat to the solitude of home.

My sister was planning to visit on her birthday in September. I had not seen Judy since she was seventeen years old; now she was forty-nine. I knew it would be a shock, but seeing her would be something from my past that I could grasp. I was curious to see if she looked like our mother, whom she had resembled as a child.

When Judy and her husband arrived I went out to meet them. She really did look like our mother. It was like seeing an older copy of my mother so many years ago. Stan didn't look like I had imagined. He had a much gentler face, with a big smile and a twinkle in his eyes. Of course my sister wanted to know what I could see. I explained that things were blurry, but I was seeing the eye chart at 20/200 and I could see the big E. I was still legally blind and might always be, but it was not the same kind of blindness. Anything was better than just seeing light and shadow. Judy asked what it was like to be able to see again. It was unbelievable, I told her, seeing my children and Anita was the most incredible thing in the world. But I was humiliated by my face. They all tried to assure me that I was OK, that I had looked that way most of my life.

"Just look at me," I said. "I have tried to shave like most people, looking in the mirror, and I couldn't stand it. I had to move back into the shower like I had shaved as a blind person." I knew I was probably harder on myself than I had to be, and I tried to listen to the people who knew me knew me for who I was, not for what I looked like.

The next morning I noticed a big change in my eyesight. I could see the grain in the kitchen cabinets. Yesterday I could see the bevels and today I could see the wood grain. I picked up the soap bottle by the sink and moved it into my limited field of vision. I could read the Palmolive bottle and the Comet cleanser can. The lettering was big so if I moved the objects in and out I could focus on them well enough to read them. It brought tears to my eyes.

Outdoors I could look at the pine trees and see the puffs of needles on them. I could distinguish objects from their background. They were flat or concave, not round or shaped correctly, but this would come in time. I decided the time had come to see if I could read the watch I had seen at Wal-Mart. We went to the store and I went to the jewelry section where my daughter's friend Chris was working. She got the watch for me and I brought it close to my face. I could see the numbers on the watch, and the minute hand and hour hand. It also had a sweeping second hand that I could see, and I promptly announced the hour, minute, and second. I began to count off the seconds as the hand moved around the watch, and I knew I had made a huge improvement. When I had first looked at this watch I couldn't see the face clearly. I bought the watch and put it in my pocket and then moved my talking watch to my other pocket. I haven't had to use it since.

Saturday was my grandson's first soccer game. When we got there Cameron came running up and asked me what I could see that day. I told him I could see a beautiful little boy in a green shirt and black shorts with knee socks and shin guards, ready to play soccer. Cameron ran onto the field and warmed up with his team, all fifteen in green shirts and black shorts. The other team wore red shirts and white shorts. I could see all this color as the boys ran up and down the field, kicking the black-and-white ball. Cameron wasn't a starter, but he played about half the game, which his team won, 6-0. I watched that game and all the rest of his games that season.

Later that day our friends Ken and Rhonda called. We had been friends for a long time, and Anita and I had taken trips with their Raindance Tour Company. They were the first of our friends that I wanted to spend time with. Everything had been overwhelming and I wanted to see a friend's face. We made a date for dinner and as they arrived I thought to myself, Here is another group of strangers I am going to have to reintroduce myself to. As they got out of the car Ken greeted me first, and I noticed that he didn't stare at my face. Then Rhonda greeted me. "Oh, hi John!" She looked exactly as I had imagined her. What a relief that a person from the past matched what I had in my mind's eye. I was no longer alone. As we talked I watched their reactions. They didn't seem to stare at my face like so many people did. I brought up the subject and told them the hardest part of all of this was looking at myself. I was having a problem with my appearance.

Ken and Rhonda looked at me. "Well John, that's who you are. Your appearance is fine with us. There is nothing the matter with you." Ken added, " You know, when you get to our age there is something the matter with all of us. That's just the way life works." Their words had such a healing effect that I began to see myself in a different view. My sister and brother-in-law had said the same thing, so this must be the way people see me.

I also began to understand what my sleeplessness was all about. Dennis Walker, the man I was in the hospital with so many years ago, was on my mind a lot. Dennis had regained his sight, only to lose it six weeks later. Like him, I felt the euphoria of seeing again and I was afraid that my sight, too, would be taken from me. Not only from me, but also from my wife, children and grandchildren. I didn't know if I could go through it again.

For my follow-up appointment with Dr. You and Dr. Cherne I asked Anita to make copies of the poster of the stork trying to eat the frog and the frog gripping the stork's throat so it couldn't swallow. I wanted to be sure to show them this twenty-year memento. They knew the poster's words had become my motto: *Never give up.* I always knew I would see again — I just never believed I would see as well as I was seeing now.

As we drove to Eugene I noticed things I hadn't seen on the previous trip. I saw letters and numbers on the street signs. I couldn't read them because of the double vision, but I could see print on the signs. I could see the road far ahead of us. I could see individual trees and tell what kind they were. They were not just a flat, greenish haze anymore. They were taking shape, and I could distinguish between fir and pine trees. The long needles on pine trees appeared as fuzzy balls. The fir needles were short, like a bottlebrush. Along the highway I could read the company name on the trucks, and sometimes even the drivers' names on the doors. I could see the highway overpasses from up to a mile away.

I walked into the building with my arm around my wife instead of holding onto her shoulder. As we waited Anita reached for a magazine and I picked one up too, the first magazine I had seen. I could see and read *Time* on the front cover with its red border. I flipped through the pages and looked at the pictures. I could read some of the ads. It was amazing. A new world had opened up to me.

During the eye test the assistant asked what I could see. I could see the large E. There was something blurry beside it but I couldn't make it out. She handed me a paddle with a hole in the center and told me to look through the hole. Now I could not only see the E but the H and D on the 20/100 line. I couldn't believe it. My vision had improved from 20/200 to 20/100 in a little over two weeks. My heart was racing. I knew I had made a tremendous breakthrough in just eighteen days. Soon there was a knock at the door and Dr. You walked in.

"I know you are here to see Dr. Cherne but I had to stop in and see you. I can't believe your eyesight is at 20/100. That is absolutely incredible. We never imagined that your sight would be this good; 20/100 is pretty good walking around vision, isn't it?"

"You better believe it," I said. "This has opened up a whole new lifestyle for me." Then I told Dr. You, "There simply aren't words in any language to express my thanks for what you have done for me."

When Dr. Cherne came in I immediately rose and shook his hand and thanked him. "Think nothing of it," he said. "It's all part of the job."

"You are much too humble," I said. "You are very gifted and I thank you from the bottom of my heart." Dr. Cherne had me put my chin in the slit lamp for the examination. He said my graft was crystal clear; there was no sign of rejection and I was weeks ahead of schedule in the healing process. I thought of my diabetes and the likelihood of slow healing, and immediately George Foreman came to mind.

"John, we won," I heard him say inside my head. "We beat this! This was the biggest fight of your life and you won." I felt such a link with the mentor I had chosen to help me become mentally prepared for this challenging ordeal. Then my attention snapped back to the present. Dr. You had looked at my retina and said things were healing fine. Dr. Cherne's results were equally good. He asked what I had been doing and as we talked he told me I was the fourth person whose sight he had restored after more than thirty years of blindness. "It doesn't happen all the time but when it does it is really gratifying."

I showed him the poster that had hung on our refrigerator for twenty years. Running my hand over it and imagining the picture and words had helped me to not give up. Now I could see it and read it and I wanted my doctors to see it, too. Dr. Cherne asked me to sign a copy for his scrapbook. "This really meant a lot to you, didn't it?"

"Yes," I told him, "it kept the fire burning to never give up."

The conversation turned to something that had been bothering me since my surgery. I wanted to know how long these procedures had been available. Dr. Cherne looked at me. "I have been performing corneal transplants in Eugene for ten years and they had been routinely doing lens transplants for three years before that."

Instantly my mind snapped into rewind and stopped in 1986. My older daughter, Heidi, had graduated from high school in 1986, and Holly had graduated two years later. Then came their weddings and the births of my grandchildren. I might have been able to see these events and share them with my family, but these procedures had never been offered to me. All at once a rage built up in me that turned into total hatred. Those cruel, insensitive, uncaring bastards at Veterans Affairs had let me be blind for thirteen years longer than necessary. Once again I felt overwhelmed — not that my vision had improved so dramatically, but because I had been denied this surgery for so long. I was sick, not for myself but for all the rest of the blinded veterans in the region.

On the way home I asked Anita if she had heard what Dr. Cherne had said.

"Yes, I did, but it may not have worked back then."

"You're right, but maybe it would have." There is no way to know, and I try not to dwell on it, but it was in my thoughts for a long time. A VA doctor had not seen me since 1988, but even in 1988 I should have been told about this surgery. There was never a word spoken about it. After twenty years, when I was permanently disabled, I was never called for physicals. They simply didn't care anymore. I was at the bottom of someone's budget. They couldn't take away my compensation so my health no longer mattered. I was never called for any eye treatment. Even with all the medical breakthroughs I was never informed of anything. Thank God for my cousin. Without him I would have spent the rest of my life blind. With God's intervention the Department of Defense took away my insurance and put me in Medicare, out of that inept system and with competent medical care.

As we drove home I tried to concentrate on the scenery. I couldn't let this consume me. I tried to start conversations with Anita that didn't seem to last long. I am sure she was overwhelmed also, but she didn't let me know. She just kept saying, "Maybe it wouldn't have worked back then." All I could think was, maybe it could have.

At home I went back into my routine of checking the pictures to test my eyesight, which was improving daily. I could see snow on the mountains and the trees were becoming clearer. I had found a new pastime — reading. I could read the headlines in our local newspaper, but some of the words didn't make sense. For example, in an article about Oregon's forests it took the longest time for the word "forest" to make sense. I could read the letters and see the word. I knew what it meant, but it took several moments for the word to sink in, to remember what a forest was and what it meant. My mind was not processing what my eye was seeing. Well, I thought, I have a huge battle to overcome and I began to work at it vigilantly. I would take out a deck of playing cards and look at the numbers and remember what they meant.

My birthday, October 4, would be the first birthday my children could get their father a birthday card that he could read instead of having someone read it to him. They had looked forward to this all their lives. Heidi's birthday was a week after mine so we planned to celebrate together, as I had a hunting trip planned and would be gone on her birthday.

We celebrated with a big cake with fifty-two candles that I could read for sure. Then it was time for the cards. Heidi and Holly had both chosen cards with large print to make it easy for me. I could read their birthday cards, and we all laughed and cried a little, for this meant so much to them. I had made huge strides lately. I could read cards, magazines, and newspapers — things I had never hoped to do. The motion sickness I had been plagued with for the last month was almost gone, although the sleeplessness persisted. I guess I was subconsciously thinking of Dennis. I only had two weeks to go and I would have six weeks of eyesight. Maybe it would stop then.

Chapter 8

A Wyoming Hunting Trip

Every fall Kenny Hutchison and I tried to take a trip together. My closest friend and hunting partner had moved to Idaho, so our hunting trips had to be long distance trips. Now, all the years that I hunted blind with Kenny sighting my gun were about to change. Long before I had ever heard of Dr. Cherne, Kenny and I had applied for an antelope-hunting license in Wyoming. In July we both received our licenses to hunt in Pinedale, Wyoming, and Kenny had made arrangements with Skinner Brothers Guide Service. We didn't know if I would be able to shoot or if Kenny would have to look through the scope and tell me when to pull the trigger. We waited as long as we could, hoping my eyesight would improve, and it had.

On October 9 Anita and I loaded our car and headed east to Klamath Falls and then into the rangeland of eastern Oregon. I had hunted there before, but it looked totally different than I had imagined. I was seeing places for the first time, and there were mountains where I thought there were plains, and gorges and giant canyons. The mountain ranges and rivers and all the fall colors were breathtaking. My head was spinning as I tried to take in everything. We crossed the Snake River and soon we were in Napa, Idaho, pulling up at Kenny's house. As I got out of the car a man who had been my friend for over twenty-five years came running down the stairs.

"What do I look like?" he asked me.

"Well Kenny, you look kind of like I thought you would but there is a little difference in your eyes. 'Course I held on to you over the years so I kind of knew what you looked like from that. It is really great to see ya, man," I said as I greeted him.

At dinner I stared at Kenny and his wife, Jackie. I had been the best man at their wedding some thirteen years before, and it was great to look on such long-term friends. We talked about the hunting trip in Wyoming, and Kenny asked how well I was seeing. I explained that I could see the crosshairs in the scope. It was blurry, but I could see them.

"That should be good enough to shoot by," he said.

The next morning we took our rifles to a rifle range to make sure they were shooting straight. Looking through the scope I could see the black bull's eye on the target. I immediately took a shot. I was six inches low and six inches to the right. I took another shot and hit the same place.

"I know the gun is shooting straight," Kenny said. "This has to be a distortion in your eye or something."

"Let me tell you something," I said. "If I have to hold a little Kentucky windage I will. That piece of paper isn't any bigger than an animal's torso. I know if I would have pulled the trigger on an animal I would have killed it."

"You're probably right," he agreed. "That target can't be any bigger than fourteen inches square, and the bull's-eye can't be any more than five inches around." Kenny made sure his rifle was sighted and we headed back to his house. We were to leave for Wyoming at three the following morning.

True to form I woke up at two-thirty and was sitting in the kitchen drinking coffee when Kenny came stumbling downstairs.

"What are you doing up at this hour?"

I explained that I couldn't sleep much past this time. "I wake up with a start and think I can't see anymore. It's been a problem," I told him, "but you can think about a lot of things while you are waiting for the rest of the world to wake up."

Kenny had coffee and we loaded his truck and took off, with me trying to see everything. I had never seen this part of the country and I wanted to see it all: the Idaho farms turning into rolling hills, then into mountains. After entering Wyoming we traveled on the Grand Teton Mountains and turned toward Pinedale and the Skinner Brothers Guide Service. Monte, the oldest of the Skinner brothers, was waiting for us at Willow Lake, twenty miles away.

There was no one in camp when we got there, so we walked down to the lake and looked around. The landscape was spectacular. The huge quaking aspen were all in gorgeous golden fall colors.

"Hello!" someone yelled. Making our way back to camp, we met Monte Skinner, our guide. He was about seventy-two years old and a veteran of many hunts. While he prepared dinner we used the target range to check our rifles. They had been bounced around in the truck and we wanted to be safe and make sure they were still shooting straight.

My gun shot perfectly for Kenny, but my shot was still six inches low and six inches to the left so I would have to use Kentucky windage. I could see the cross hairs in the rifle and the target at 100 yards with the rifle at 7 power, so I knew I would be able to make the shot if I was given the opportunity.

At dinner Monte told us it wouldn't be hard to find antelope. We knew this was true because we had seen several herds of antelope, some with as many as fifty. They looked like herds of sheep wandering the prairie.

We went to bed early, as breakfast was at four-thirty. The next morning we ate heartily, knowing it might be a long time before lunch if we had to pack an antelope out of the woods. We put on our orange hunting vests, grabbed our rifles and drove slowly toward the main road just as daylight appeared. We hadn't been out of camp for ten minutes when Monte pointed out a buck antelope on the ridge. Kenny saw it, but it was still too dark for me to see that far.

"Let me get out of the truck," I said, "and if I can see him with my scope I might just open the season a little early." I put my rifle on the hood of the truck and looked through it. As luck would have it the antelope was in the bottom of my scope. All I had to do was lower the scope a little and he was dead center. His horns were a little bigger than his ears but that was good enough for me. This was the one I wanted. I made the adjustment for Kentucky windage and shot, then I heard Kenny's war hoop as he jumped out of the truck. I put the safety on my rifle and laid it on the hood of the truck and Kenny and I started jumping around and dancing patting each other on the back. After all these years I had shot this animal completely by myself.

"This only happens in dreams, John," he said. We checked that the antelope was dead and estimated the size. "After measuring fish for so long I would say the horns are about thirteen inches." He was hoping he would get one as big.

We dressed the animal and got the meat into Monte's cooler quickly. My hunting season had lasted all of ten minutes with a spectacular ending. It was October 11, my daughter's thirty-first birthday and exactly forty-five days after my surgery. I had gone from only seeing light and dark to being able to shoot a gun proficiently.

We hunted two more days, and Kenny got his antelope. It wasn't as large as mine but a beautiful animal all the same. After all the years of stories of the one that got away or the one that we missed we both had antelope from our Wyoming hunting trip.

Back in Napa, Kenny and I hugged and wiped tears from our eyes as I loaded the car, knowing it would be another year before we hunted together again. There is no one closer than two hunting partners, not even brothers. Kenny and I are like brothers — not by blood, but by love.

I was up early again the next morning and had coffee waiting for everyone else. After breakfast Anita and I started for home, following the same route. When we pulled into Grants Pass I noticed things were clearer than when I left. My vision was changing more slowly now, but from our driveway I could see farther in the distance. Inside the house the pictures were a lot clearer. What I had taken for one tree in the painting of the Grand Tetons was actually two trees close together. The yellow brush in the lower corner was quaking aspens with their white trunks, beautifully done in fall colors. I was amazed at how much my vision had improved in the last nine days.

A few weeks later I had a follow-up eye exam, and I brought pictures from my hunting trip to show Dr. Cherne and the staff. He was amazed to hear about all I had seen and done in the past month. During the exam he found the cornea graft crystal-clear, with no sign of rejection. The retina, too, was still holding firm. During the vision test I saw the 20/100 line very well, some of the 20/80 line and less of the 20/60 line. As Dr. Cherne and I talked I took out my pocket watch.

"Remember when I brought this watch last time? I could see the numbers and the hands," I reminded him. "I took it hunting with me and on a clear day I could read 'Remington' at the bottom of the watch. It also says 'Since 1816' on it."

"Let me see that." Dr. Cherne reached into his desk and took out a card. He wanted me to see if I could read the words, which were the size of 20/40 print. I held it about six inches from my face and moved it until it came into focus. Dr. Cherne was amazed: I could read almost all the 20/40 letters. Everything was going great, he said, and he wanted to see me in two months instead of one month. Next time he would try to remove some stitches to help me see better. Then he put his hand on my shoulder.

"John, I truly believe you are going to be legally blind after all this due to the field of vision you have."

"If this is blind," I told him, "I don't remember blind." I was so elated with my eyesight that thirty-one years of only seeing light was a distant memory now.

My next appointment was with Dr. Tanczos. When I stepped on the scales I weighed 185 pounds. All the diet and exercise had paid off. I had lost forty-five pounds since February, and my blood pressure and blood sugar were also down.

"I don't have to read this to you. You can read it yourself." Dr. Tanczos handed me my test results and I positioned the paper so I could read it. The serum hemoglobin, measuring the sugar carried in the blood, was 5.9; anything above 7 is diabetic, so mine was well within normal range.

After such a positive check-up there was just one remaining problem. I asked Dr. Tanczos if he knew of a plastic surgeon who could help my face.

"I can see myself in the mirror now, and it isn't pleasant." He tried to assure me that I didn't look so bad, but I knew he was being kind. He promised to look into it.

Chapter 9

Finding My Place in a New World

Our friends Ken and Rhonda had a trip to Reno and Las Vegas planned in November and wanted us to go with them. I hadn't seen Las Vegas since Anita and I were married there, nearly thirty-two years before. I immediately said yes. I knew it was no longer the sleepy little town it had been when we were there, and I wanted to see the lights of Las Vegas.

We spent the first night in Reno, then drove on to Las Vegas and the Mirage Hotel the next morning. We arrived, checked in, and made plans for the evening. I felt like a hayseed coming to town in a load of pumpkins, I told Ken, but I just wanted to walk around and see everything.

I walked up and down the strip, in and out of all the casinos, and I watched people playing slot machines and cards. It was all so much to take in, I told Anita that night. It was an unbelievable experience. She asked what I wanted to do the next day, and I told her I really wanted to see the medieval show at the Excalibur. I was always interested in knights when I was a kid and it sounded very entertaining.

"Well if that is what you want to do we ought to do it." So I went to sleep with dreams of knights and swords and bright flashing lights, until I woke up at three-thirty, as usual. This sleeplessness wouldn't even leave me on trips.

We got up the next morning and walked around town again. It wasn't nearly as pretty as it was at night, when you can see lights for miles and miles in every direction. That evening we got a cab to the Excalibur to see the show. There were costumes and lights and swords, and the area was set up like King Arthur's court. It was magnificent. Afterwards we took a cab downtown and enjoyed the light show set to music in old Las Vegas. That night I told Anita about all I had seen. Only one thing was not going well on this trip, I told her.

"I feel like I'm around strangers. People don't know me. They look at me like I'm something different. Like a freak at a sideshow. I don't know why, but when people see me their mouths fall open and they stare at me as I walk by. It's happened several times on this trip," I said. "I know you are probably used to it, Anita, and I am sorry." It really hurt and bothered me, but there was nothing I could do. I was so happy about being able to see, yet I was also miserable.

Early in the morning of November 25 my daughter Heidi called.

"Dad, one of my friends just called and your and Mom's picture is all over the front page of *The Oregonian*. It's a huge article with a big picture of you and Mom at the top."

"You have to be kidding me," I said. Beth Quinn had done the interview for the story about regaining my eyesight. She said it would be a big article but I didn't know it would be front page.

"It is," Heidi said. "It's all over the front page." Our Thanksgiving had started with a bang.

Anita and I drove to Holly and Cole's house, and my son-in-law drove me to the newsstand to get extra copies. Inside the store was a huge stack of *Oregonians* on the shelf, and there I was on the front page, with my beautiful wife, in living color. I picked up six or eight and took them to the counter.

"Hey, that's you isn't it?" the man asked. "Well, congratulations." I told him it had been a long time coming.

Back at Holly's I sat down and tried to read the article, but my eyes filled with tears. I saw that they had touched up the photo, as

I had requested, so the discoloration wasn't so severe around my eyes. I asked Anita to read so I could hear the story. As she began my tears welled up again and I blinked them away. Seeing the huge photo on the front page was like seeing a dream come true. I am sure that every blind person in the world hopes to live the event that was happening to me. Seeing the photo touched me in ways I could only dream about. I not only got to see the photo of this person whose vision had been miraculously restored, but also a glimpse of what he dreamt his face would look like someday. A look at the past as well as the future.

As Anita read I began to relive the events that began with the explosion on September 17, 1968. Being slammed against the wall, trying to silhouette my hands in front of my face. Looking through the yellow hue and seeing their awful condition. The ride to the hospital was as fresh as if it had happened yesterday, but it had been thirty-one years ago. I recalled relating to Beth Quinn how I felt invincible at age twenty. I thought my eyes were full of dirt and after they were washed out things would be OK. As Anita read on the story moved to my hospitalization and attempted treatment at Fitzsimmons General Hospital and how after nine months I realized I was not responding to treatment and I would be blind for the rest of my life. I had told my attending physician, Let's turn the page and move on. I had a child and hopes of having more children and I would have to do the best that I could.

Anita read the account of my seeing our children for the very first time, Heidi at age thirty-one and Holly at age twenty-nine. Heidi had been born just twenty-four days after the explosion. The story followed our life on the farm, raising animals and vegetables, and teaching my children these skills as I mastered them myself as a blind person in a sighted world.

Despite being told that nothing could be done to restore my sight I never gave up hope, until finally I found my way to the Clear Vision Institute in Eugene, Oregon. There Dr. Scott Cherne determined that my cornea was opaque — he couldn't see in and I couldn't see out — but there was no major damage to my retina. With those two factors he felt I had a chance for some improvement in my vision; how much they didn't know.

Reliving all this was painful at times and wonderful at times. How the Lions Eye Bank of Oregon helps the loved ones of donors work through their grief and bring some good from their loss. The Lions Eye Bank supplies 500 corneas to 40 surgeons in Oregon and Southwest Washington for transplant, with a 95 percent success rate. Today's improved surgical techniques offer hope to people who have been blind for many years.

I was one of those recipients. The Lions in Oregon had provided me with the priceless gift of a cornea, generously given by a young man about my own daughters' age who had been killed in an accident. Always the thought is in my mind: This young man could have been my son.

My family and I relived the uncertainty during and after the surgery, as Dr. Timothy You found my retina was detached and had shown blast damage that was not detected by ultrasound. The next unexpected development was the discovery of a sliver of wood piercing my lens that had been there for thirty years, eleven months, and seven days. After my lens was replaced with a man-made lens, Dr. Scott Cherne used sutures finer than hair to attach the donated cornea. Anita and Holly recalled how Dr. Cherne had looked afterwards, visibly tired and so unsure of his results. He had told them maybe I'd see motion, at best, but despite his grim prognosis we managed to cling to hope. The moment of truth came the next morning when Dr. You removed the bandage. After the intense blast of light I could see Dr. You's wristwatch as the bandage was pulled away. As the story unfolded I went from a twenty-year-old army medic to a nearly fifty-two-year-old white-haired grandfather with a scarred face. And now I could see my beautiful wife, who had taken the image of her mother, and my two beautiful daughters whose beauty I had only known by touch or speech and who looked so much like their mother in her youth.

The story closed with our thoughts for the future, beginning with Thanksgiving and then the most wonderful wedding anniversary and Christmas, getting to see my family open their gifts. All this because a young man I never met had the foresight to donate his cornea so that a blind man could see.

I was so pleased with the article, and I truly believe Beth Quinn, the reporter, deserves an award for her work. *The Oregonian* article took up the entire front page, and on that day there wasn't anything about a hurricane or a bombing or some calamity that caused death or destruction. It was a story about giving and about something good coming from pain and loss. We were all quiet, wondering how many of our friends would read the article and learn I had gotten my sight back.

Soon both daughters were in the kitchen helping their mother prepare our Thanksgiving feast while grandchildren played in the living room and my son-in-law and I watched the football game on TV. I was seeing all this for the first time — my children's faces at the dinner table along with my grandchildren and my son-in-law and my beautiful wife at my side for this wonderful meal. As the meal ended I reminded them all that we had much to be thankful for.

Back home our message machine was completely full, and the next day the calls continued. Friends had seen the article, including some I had not seen for many years. They all called to congratulate me, and once again I felt fortunate to have these wonderful people as friends.

The young man's family had also seen the article, and a few days later I received a beautiful letter from the wife of the donor. I still have the letter and I always will. The Associated Press picked up the story, and it soon went around the world. I received phone calls from complete strangers, saying they had never done this before but wanted to wish me luck with the rest of my life. These calls of support meant a lot to me.

My vision was improving, and things were going well. The only problem was when I looked in the mirror I could still see my face. One December morning I was sitting in the living room drinking coffee and listening to the radio, when I heard an ad for facial plastic surgery. I felt it was heaven-sent, and I bolted out of the chair and kept repeating the name so Anita could look it up and call for an appointment. As soon as I hung up the phone a calm came over me. I knew there would be something they could do for my face. I would not have to spend the rest of my life looking like this.

At my next eye appointment there was a huge improvement. As we waited I picked up magazines — I could read *Sports Illustrated, Time, American Rifleman,* and *Better Homes and Gardens,* the big lettering at least, and sometimes the captions under the photos. When it was time to read the eye chart I could see the big E and the 20/100 line; next I could read the 20/80 line. Using the paddle with the hole in it I could see the 20/60 line and some of the 20/50 line. When Dr. Cherne came in he said, "Your vision has improved to 20/80, John, that's pretty good. If you had glasses it would be even better." He examined my eye and said, "Your graft is crystal clear. There is no sign of rejection." We chatted about *The Oregonian* article and I told him I wanted people to know about the new technologies — people like me who were told years ago that they would never be able to see and now there might be hope.

The following week I met with Dr. Stephen Guggenheim. I explained that Dr. Wheatley had seen me in this office years ago and had done some dermabrasion and other surgeries on my face but it had left scars and I wanted to see if they could be removed. Dr. Guggenheim moved closer and began a meticulous study of my face, pinching and then stretching the skin to study it.

"I am sure there is something that can be done for your face, John." He explained that the procedure required a certain laser, "but I don't want you to give up."

Things were very busy that December. Anita and the girls had transformed our house into a lovely Christmas scene. Holly and Anita went to the end of our property to find the best Christmas tree — one that would fill the living room — and decorated it with lights and a lovely angel on top. And I was like a child of three or four — I had to touch everything.

Once the scene was set for the holiday it was time to get the gifts. Christmas Eve is our wedding anniversary and I wanted it to be very special so I asked my son-in-law Cole to take me shopping in Medford.

We found the store I was looking for and I went to the jewelry counter and asked to see a certain ring with two pearls, one black and one white. I told Cole I wanted to give this ring to Anita for our anniversary to symbolize something. The black pearl is for the thirty-one years that I didn't get to see Anita and the white one was for the rest of our lives that I will get to see her. I had been blinded shortly before our first wedding anniversary, I told him, and I had never been able to pick out a gift for her all by myself. I wanted it to be special. I bought the ring for our anniversary plus a necklace to go with it for Anita's Christmas gift.

There would be a lot of "firsts" this Christmas. Seeing my wife open her anniversary gift, my children opening their gifts, and the faces of my grandchildren, much like my children when they were little. All the things I had missed with my own children. As I sat and looked at our tree in the days before Christmas I tried to remember the Christmases of the past. Our first Christmas when I had hitchhiked home and made Anita my wife. Our second Christmas, right after I had been blinded and we had celebrated it at her cousin's house. Our third Christmas in our own home, waiting for the tuition approval letter that never came. Then the Christmases with our children on the two farms we had lived on. Oh what a string of wonderful times I had missed. It occurred to me that as a blind person you really only live half a life. You have to imagine everything, and some things you get right and others are way off. You try to grab the best things and fit them into your world. Sometimes it's the only way to hold onto reality.

It was the tradition in our house to open our gifts on Christmas Eve. The children and grandchildren would come for cookies and eggnog and soup. It was also a tradition that Anita and I would exchange anniversary gifts at two o'clock, the time we had said our marriage vows all those years ago. I had read through probably a hundred cards to find the right words to say to my lovely wife. It was a little early, but I went to the bedroom and got the box with the ring and an envelope containing my hand-picked card. Anita was looking out the window.

"I can't stand it anymore," I told her. "I want to present you with your anniversary gift." I watched as she opened the card and read it, then smiled at me. As she opened the box I told her, "Anita, this ring means a great deal to me. I picked this out to symbolize my love for you. The black pearl symbolizes the thirty-one years I could not see your lovely face. The white pearl symbolizes the rest of my life that I can." Tears ran down her face, then she went to get my gift. I opened the card and read the message of her love for me. Tears filled my eyes and I had to put the card down. This was the first time I had ever read what I meant to her. She signed her card with love and across the bottom she wrote, "I hope you don't ever have to pawn this one!!!" I didn't know what she meant, but slowly I began to unwrap the small, hinged box. Inside was a Seiko wrist-watch, exactly like the one I had pawned to marry her.

This wonderful woman had taken the first opportunity to replace the only possession of value that I had owned as a vagabond soldier. Giant sobs came out of my body. I had never experienced anything so wonderful in all my life. This woman who had given me two children and shared all the ups and downs in my life had reached a new plateau in my heart. After thirty-two years I thought I had known this woman, but this gesture of her love for me was overwhelming. I sat and looked at this watch and cried and cried. Then I got up and hugged her. "I hope we both live a long life, Anita, so that I can look upon your face forever." I placed the ring on her finger and she helped me adjust the watchband on my arm. Then we hugged again and from that point on I looked at my wife with different eyes. Little did I know that my children also had a special surprise for me.

As they arrived we showed them our anniversary gifts. They were touched deeply by the symbols of the love that we shared. Soon we finished the soup and sandwiches and moved into the living room to pass out gifts. This was the time I had been waiting for, to see their faces as they opened our gifts. Packages were passed around, but I simply sat and watched for the most part. I wanted to see their expressions as they ripped open the wrapping and then watch the Ohs and Ahs, for I had missed this with my children. Then Anita opened the necklace I had bought and one of our daughters helped her put it on. Suddenly everyone noticed I hadn't opened anything yet. All eyes were on me as I unwrapped a lovely shirt from Anita and some very special gifts from my daughters. They had gone through all the family pictures and made an album of their lives from the time they were babies to small children, then to adolescents and young adults, ending with their wedding pictures. A complete pictorial record of their lives.

Then came two special gifts. First was an alarm clock with two-inch-high letters, the cure for my sleepless nights. When I woke up I could just look across the room and know I could still see. I didn't have to jump up and run in the bathroom to check. This has allowed me to sleep till four-thirty or five every morning. Although I still wake up two or three times at night I look at the clock and say to myself, Yep, things are still working, and go back to sleep.

Next came another very special gift. While they were gathering pictures my daughters had run across one of the few snapshots that Anita's mother had taken on the day we were married. They had it enlarged and put it in a beautiful silver frame. As I opened it my God, all the years raced back. There stood a young man and a beautiful young woman with so much hope in their faces and so full of life, wondering what the future would bring. Even more, this picture of Anita was exactly how I remembered her for thirty-one years. Again sobs came out of my body and tears ran down my face and splashed onto the glass and the frame.

I wiped my eyes and told the girls what a wonderful thing they had done. I start and end each day looking at that picture, and I will do so every day for the rest of my life. Both daughters wiped tears from their eyes and we all had a drink and wished each other well for the year that was coming upon us.

At this point Cole told us all that after thinking it over he had accepted a job in Las Vegas and would be leaving on the fourth of January. We all congratulated him for we all knew what this meant to his and Holly's future. She was an important part of our lives for twenty-nine years and now she was moving with her husband and child. We assured Cole that he needed to make this move for his future and also Holly's. They weren't moving away, we told them — they were giving us a destination. We now had a sunny place to go during the dreary Oregon winters.

Soon it was time to take the grandkids home and prepare for Santa's visit during the night. Anita and I put the house in order and slowly made our way to bed. We looked at one another with huge smiles and hugged and touched each other and made love very tenderly, just like it was the first time. Two people with an all-consuming love who knew they would spend the rest of their lives together.

Morning started with early calls from our grandchildren telling of the gifts Santa had brought. Anita got up and in her usual style on holidays, she started cooking like she had done for so many years with her mother. All the holidays brought back memories of Anita's mother. She was such a wonderful person, and I missed her at these times, especially this year. I wished she could have shared all that had happened to me. She had been so supportive all the years I had been blind.

On Christmas Day my grandchildren brought all their new toys, and I sat and watched them play while my daughters helped Anita prepare the traditional prime rib feast. We were all feeling blessed for the things that had been bestowed on us. I knew that God had fixed my eyes and that soon I would get help for my face. The following week I learned that I would see Dr. Douglas Naversen and Dr. J. David Igelman in January. It was a huge step forward in the new millennium.

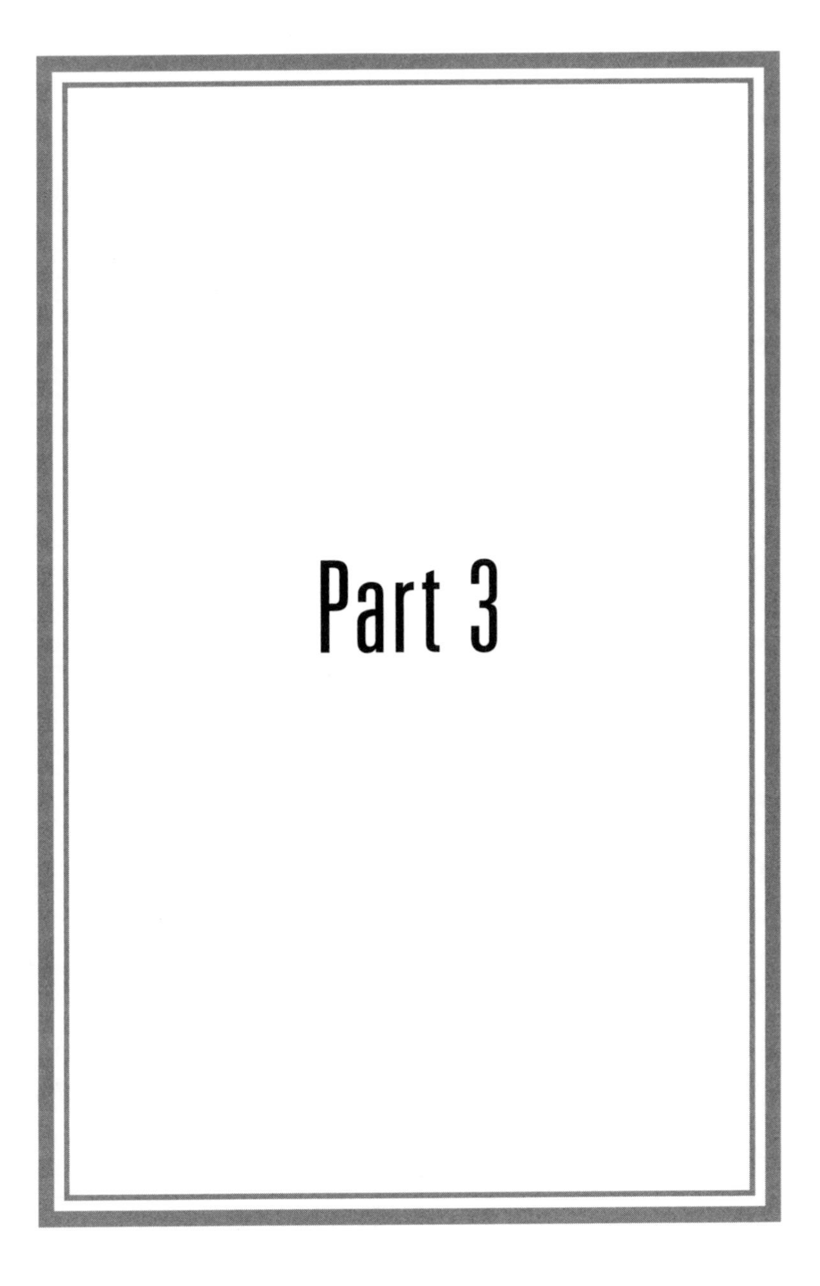

Part 3

Chapter 10

Now I See How I Look

January 1, 2000 came to Murphy, Oregon, as it did around the rest of the world, with no major calamities. The banks still had money; the gas stations had gas — no major disasters anywhere. The only sad note at our house was the departure of our son-in-law, Cole Wilson, who was moving to Las Vegas the next day for his new job. We were happy about this career opportunity, but we were also sad also that we would not be able to see the kids as often.

I had three weeks before my appointment to see about getting treatment for my face, and the only thing until then was helping Holly get their family moved to Nevada. So when my friend Ken called to ask Anita and me to join him and Rhonda on a trip it was an easy decision. We would fly from San Francisco to Cancun, Mexico, and then go by ship to Cozumel, then to Honduras, over to Roatan Bay Island, up to the Grand Caymans, then to Jamaica and return to Cancun and home.

The price was right, and this was a trip both of us had wanted to do for many years. Besides, Anita said, "if we stay home all we'll do is sit here and stew over what the doctors are going to say about your face." She was right. January 24 seemed like six months away, so I called Ken and said we were free.

"I just called the travel agent," Ken said. "If you want to go we'll leave Friday. We'll be gone for eight days and have the time of our lives. We can go find the sunshine and get out of this rain."

We did join Ken and Rhonda and Ron and Diane, her parents, and had a wonderful week. The only negative note was that I received a lot of stares and second looks because of my face. I was a real eyesore.

When we returned Cole had found three houses that he wanted Holly to see, so we were going to have our grandson Cameron for five glorious days before he moved away. We took him to school and played games with him and just enjoyed spending time with him, as we knew this would not happen as often as it had in the past.

The time passed quickly with our grandson and soon the day came for my appointment. I awoke at four-thirty, very apprehensive. I was hopeful that something could be done for my face, but in the back of mind I kept thinking, I was very lucky with my eye — maybe there is nothing they can do about my face. Then again, maybe they can. The question plagued me.

It's about an hour's drive from Murphy to Medford. Anita tried to make conversation and I would answer, but I was mostly quiet, thinking about the appointment. The chance to get help and improve my life meant so much to me, and I was afraid I'd be disappointed.

When we arrived at Dermatology and Laser Associates of Medford I checked in at the reception desk. "Oh, you are here from a referral from Dr. Guggenheim," the receptionist said.

"Yes, I am. I am here to see if there is anything they can do for my face."

"If there is anyone who can, Mr. Malkow, it is these doctors." There were forms to sign and insurance cards needed. I didn't know which of the five cards she would want. I had two from Veterans Affairs for their hospitals and one for outpatient services, a Medicare card and one from Tricare for my military benefits. Most recently, Medicare and Tricare had covered my eye surgery, so she took those to copy. Soon a young woman called my name and escorted us back to an examination room.

I sat on the exam table and Anita took a chair. In a few moments there was a knock at the door and a man about my age introduced himself.

"Hi John, I am Dr. Douglas Naversen and this is my associate, Dr. David Igelman. Kathy Kenaston is our office manger, a nurse and a laser technician, and Sharon Bauer, at the end, is also a laser tech. We are all here to take a look at you. Dr. Guggenheim said you were an interesting case and I can see what he means. We don't see many people like you."

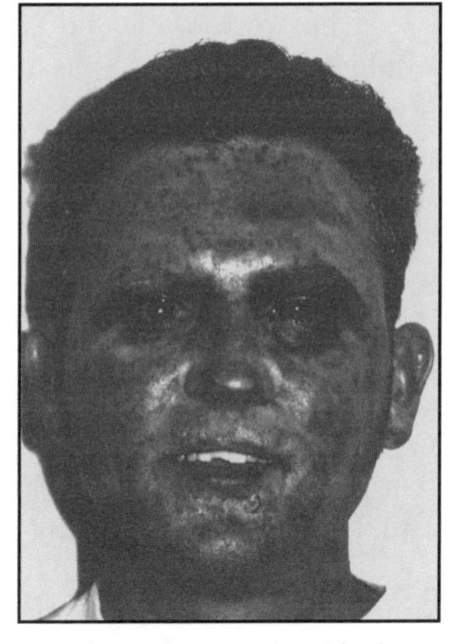

By age twenty-nine, I had undergone five dermabrasion treatments to remove the discoloration caused by the chemicals in the blast.

I told him I was sure he didn't, that this was an ongoing thing and I had hoped his new lasers would help. Both Dr. Naversen and Dr. Igelman assured me there was help, that my situation was exactly what the new laser equipment had been developed for. Then Dr. Naversen started his examination. He would take my skin in his fingers and pinch it lightly, observing every reaction to his touch. Then it was Dr. Igelman's turn, again pinching and poking and touching, all the time observing and recording the skin's reactions. Both doctors agreed that I could be helped but they wanted to take a biopsy of my skin to see how deep the marks were. The VersaPulse C laser was capable of going .07 mm deep, exploding the molecules in the pigment and making it small enough for the white blood cells to carry to my lymph nodes. The laser treatment actually sets up an inflammation, which calls the blood cells to work. The material wouldn't actually be removed, but it would be carried off to be stored in the lymph nodes. This is how all infections are taken care of in the body, whether viral or bacterial. It's a way to use white blood cells in another capacity besides fighting infection.

The work would be done by the laser technicians, and it would be a lengthy process, but their words were what I wanted to hear. I told them about the explosion and what I had endured and the types of chemicals involved in the blast so they could determine the best treatment. I told them of Dr. Wheatley's treatments, the chemical burns and acid peels, and all he had done to get my face to its current condition.

"I am quite sure that Michael Wheatley saved my life," I told them. "If he hadn't told me I was freckled I am sure I would have saved my family all these years of embarrassment by simply ending my life." But now there was hope. I could have this staining and scarring removed from my face and I would look like everyone else. Dr. Naversen patted my shoulder.

"John, we can take this off your face and when I am done with you, you will look like a movie star." This very caring physician had worked with injuries and birthmarks and other kinds of disfigurements and was very sensitive to people's feelings, knowing these feelings went right to a person's very soul.

"We want to make sure how far this is blasted into your skin, so we want to do biopsies and take some of the skin and look at it under a microscope. That will tell us the right setting on the laser so we can be right into it." I agreed, and Kathy led me into another treatment room where Dr. Igelman removed two samples for microscopic study. Then pictures were taken for comparison later. That completed the exam, pending insurance approval for the treatments.

It was an enormous relief, and Anita and I talked excitedly all the way home. I didn't know what the treatment would be like, but I was ready to endure anything to remove those awful scars.

The next day I received a telephone call from Jeff Clark, an insurance agent we had known years before. He was a member of the Grants Pass Lions Club and was calling to ask if I would come to the next Lions meeting and talk about what it was like to get my sight back. "I saw the article in the paper," he said, "and I was simply amazed."

I told him I would be happy to tell them how I got my sight back and the feeling of seeing my family for the first time and some of the things I had done. I asked if he wanted me to bring my daughter Heidi to explain what it was like to have a dad that did things as a normal sighted person now, after thirty-one years. "That would be great," he said, and we confirmed the date.

My vision had been about the same for the past few months. I could still read if I held the paper just right, and I could get around fairly well. After all those years, I felt I was truly blessed. Every day I would tell Anita that even if it didn't get any better I would always be thankful. There would be some little change, maybe just seeing things again and my brain processing the information, and it began to get easier and easier. My sleeping habits were a lot better now, thanks to the clock Anita had given me. It stood there every night like a beacon, assuring me that I could still see. I wake up at eleven-thirty and three-thirty each night, sleeping till four-thirty or five at the very latest, but I don't have to get out of bed and run to the bathroom anymore. I simply look up and see my old buddy telling me what time it is.

I hadn't seen Dr. Tanczos in nearly three months and it was time to check on my general health. When Dr. Tanczos came in he asked what I had been doing. I told him about Christmas and what it was like to see my family open their gifts for the first time. I showed him the beautiful watch from Anita, and I told him I had been to see Dr. Naversen and Dr. Igelman and they were going to be able to remove the scarring on my face with laser treatments. Dr. Tanczos was very happy with my progress in the last year.

"John, your health is excellent right now. You weighed in at 182 pounds this morning; you have lost 49 pounds, my friend, and you look the peak of health." I was really happy about that. I hadn't looked at a scale — I was simply following the diet and exercising daily, and it was working for me. Then he had some sad news. The clinic was going to be closed, and the four doctors would be leaving for other positions. "I would like to open a private practice but I am financially unable to do that, John. I owe a lot of money for my education loans."

I told him I would miss him. He had done more for my overall health than any doctor in thirty years, treating my cholesterol and helping me achieve good health. I felt he was a major part of the rapid healing after my eye surgery. He had gotten my diabetes under control and my cholesterol and blood pressure where they belonged and now I was in good health.

"I can't take all the credit, John. I can give you the treatment but if you don't follow it, it won't work. You have taken control of your health. You have done what I have told you; the medicine only helps." Dr. Tanczos got up and hugged me. "John, every doctor has patients they never forget and I will never forget you."

I told him I would probably not be the last blind patient he ever had and I had a request: that if he had blind patients, to make sure that at least every eighteen months they would be seen by a *competent* eye surgeon, at a *competent* clinic, so their eyesight could be restored if at all possible. He promised me he would do so. I bid Dr. Tanczos farewell and good luck in his new job and I left thinking, What am I going to do without this talented young man in my life? I needed a doctor and I didn't know where I would find one.

Heidi was excited about telling the Lions group what it was like not only to have a blind dad but now to have one who could see. It was an experience that not everyone lived through. I told her that we had an exceptional story and we needed to share it, especially with the people in our hometown. By February 1 we were ready. We met Jeff Clark, who took us through the buffet line for lunch. Then the meeting began and it was our turn. I hadn't spoken to a group since I was in the Army, making announcements and giving instructions, but this was a lot different and thirty-one years had gone by. At first it felt like an awful experience. Standing up there, I felt every eye on me but then, as my story unfolded I saw that people were very interested. They worked hard as Lions volunteers, and they needed to see the results of their work — not just a letter of thanks, but a chance to see and hear someone they had helped. Every person in the audience, at one time or another, had transported a cornea to the Oregon Eye Bank from which I had received my cornea. A calm came over me as I told my story — the explosion of light that hit me, seeing Dr. You's watch after the transplant surgery, looking across the room and seeing images of my family waiting there, then the ride home and being able to see the bathroom and not having to use my cane anymore. Soon I saw people reaching for their handkerchiefs and wiping their eyes. I spoke of the feeling of seeing my wife and children, what it was like to see Anita's face after thirty-one years, and seeing my children for the very first time. Having a wonderful Christmas with my family, watching them open their Christmas gifts for the very first time. Playing with my grandchildren and watching my grandson play soccer and looking at the artwork my granddaughter makes for me. I explained how my eye had changed, how you don't see very well at first; everything is blurry and then it slowly comes into focus. I finished by telling them about my recent good news, that all my facial scars and pigment would be removed and how fortunate I was, because my sole desire was to be an individual just like them.

Then it was Heidi's turn. She talked about what it was like for her dad, and her feelings when I looked at her for the very first time with her sister Holly, and how happy they were for what the Lions had given our family with the cornea. None of this would have been possible without them. Afterwards everyone came up and congratulated us and welcomed us.

Heidi and I were both enthusiastic about the work the Lions do. We both thought it would be wonderful to join the Lions and help people like me and others with sight and hearing dysfunction to get eyeglasses or hearing aids or corneas. So my daughter and I were the new Lions in February. I have since attended a lot of Lions functions, and I know these people care. Their whole life is to care and serve. They work in so many ways behind the scenes, never asking for thanks. That is the Lions motto: We Serve.

A few days later Anita went down to get the mail and came back with a huge smile on her face. "You look like you have a check for ten thousand dollars," I said.

"No, I think it's a little better than that." She produced a copy of a letter from Dr. Naversen to Dr. Guggenheim with the results of the biopsy, indicating that the deepest pigment in my skin was .03 millimeters. The VersaPulse laser could reach .07 millimeters so this was well within the range, meaning that all the pigment could be removed.

I was ecstatic. This meant there would be no remnants left this time. After all the face grindings and acid treatments, I still looked terrible. This news was comparable to having my sight restored. Now I would not only see again, but I would have a chance to live my life as a normal human being, not to be stared at like a circus sideshow. After all these years everything could be erased. I might be able to live my life as a normal human being.

The next morning the Laser Associates office called. "John, I don't know how to tell you this but both Medicare and Tricare have turned you down for facial treatments," Kathy said. "They say it is cosmetic, and they will not pay for it."

"What do you want to do, John?"

"I don't know what to tell you," I said. "Let me have the weekend to think about it. I am a disabled veteran and now the Medicare and Tricare people don't want to take care of me like they promised they would. The ink is barely dry on my Medicare card and I have already been turned down. Still, I was awarded a service-connected disability from this injury. My God, someone has to do something. Let me think about and we can apply to the VA, but I don't know what good it will do. I'll come in Monday and we'll go over what we need to do next."

This was a new development in my experience with the government. These people now were charging me for turning me down. Before it had all been part of my benefits. I was paying just like everyone else for the pleasure of being turned down for service-connected disabilities. I was sick at the stomach. Somehow fair no longer fit in the process. My faith again dwindled in the United States government. How could they turn me down for something as severe as I was going through? The people — those bean counters — who make the decisions need to wear someone's face or live with these disabilities before they call them cosmetic. Facial disfigurements, to the general public, are seen as uncleanness. *The person is seen as unclean.*

Saturday and Sunday were very quiet at our house. I stewed and mulled, and Anita was just taken aback. How could anyone be treated this way? I didn't know what to say. I didn't have any answers anymore. I had been told so many things and lied to so many times, I didn't trust anyone in the government anymore.

Monday morning I was wide-awake at three-thirty. I had dug out the information to tell Kathy how to apply for veterans' benefits on a fee basis, but I suspected it was next to worthless. I was deep in thought as Anita and I drove to Medford. I had hoped things would change but they hadn't, so now we would go back and try to get things done through the VA.

At the office Kathy asked what we wanted to do. She had a smile, but she could see the despair on my face. "Kathy," I told her, "someone in the government really needs to do his or her job. I was hurt when I was in the service, before my twenty-first birthday. These people need to take care of me. I am the type of person they built the Veterans department for. I was a one hundred percent blinded disabled veteran for thirty-one years. I gave the sacrifice, maybe it wasn't the ultimate sacrifice, but the price I paid with thirty-one years of darkness was very severe. I can't believe the way the government is treating me, but after all these years what else was I to expect? You go ahead and apply at the Roseburg fee basis office and we will see what we get."

While we waited for the reply I had another eye appointment. During the drive to Eugene I pointed out things to Anita that I couldn't see on the last trip, two months ago. The trees had become round and I could see farther up the highway. The distant street signs were much easier to see, but I still had double vision when the letters and numbers came closer. I later learned that this was all part of the cornea transplant process; my eye was shaped more like a football than a basketball. This is astigmatism and it can be cured with glasses, but it can also be helped by removing some of the stitches that hold the cornea in place, lessening the tension so it can expand or contract to the desired shape. This appointment was to see if Dr. Cherne could remove some of the stitches and take away this double vision and improve my overall vision. I knew my vision had improved. I could see farther, and I could see more clearly. Also, I guess the information that was transmitted to my brain was finally sinking in. Going through the same towns that we had traveled through so many times since the operation it was obvious that things were improving.

I was to see Dr. You first and then Dr. Cherne. Anita and I walked down the hall into the exam room and soon Dr. You walked in. I stood up and hugged the young man who had repaired my retina.

"It is so good to see you walking around and doing what you're doing, John." I told him that he had changed my life, and related what I had done since I last saw him in October. I told him about the hunting trip to Wyoming and the trips to Las Vegas and the Caribbean, and what a wonderful Christmas I had had with my children and grandchildren. I told him how my vision had changed, and I showed him I could read 20/40 print and make out all the letters.

"I want both of you to know that this is a miracle," he said. "You have no idea what it is like to see you doing what you are doing, John." Then he put on his observation light and got his large lens to check the retina. Everything looked perfect but he wanted me to know there was no need to worry if I developed problems. Not only was he able to transplant retinas, he explained. "We are only a couple years away from transplanting a whole eye. So don't worry about losing your sight."

Then Dr. You sat down next to me. "John, I want to talk to you about your prosthetic eye. There is a new prosthetic eye available. The one you have is rather poor." I had noticed this also; it was rather large and the wrong color. It was a real headlight, and it went right along with the rest of my face. He told me it was possible now to make an eye that would attach to the muscles that control the eye, which would give it complete movement. It was made of materials that looked real enough to fool him, and the eye movement tracks just like the real eye. I thanked him and said I had a lot of regret about my face and my eye was certainly part of it. When I told him of seeing the doctor to have the tattooing and scarring removed from my face he cautioned me to make sure they use an eye shield to protect it.

Next a technician took us to a room with a topography machine. It uses sonic waves to make a map of the surface of the eye and prints it out in a graph. The image looks like a topographical map with lines for different heights to show the exact shape of your eye. This is done after a cornea transplant to reveal where to remove the sutures to shape the cornea and correct the astigmatism as well as nearsightedness and farsightedness.

Then it was my favorite time: reading the eye chart. I sat back in the chair and she dimmed the lights and put up the eye chart. There was the big E then the H and B. Next came the 20/80 line, and I could see some of the 20/60 line. The letters were blurry but I could make them out. She then gave me the paddle and I began to read the 20/60 line, then the 20/50 line and the 20/40 line. I was so excited, and as I was reading I could hear the excitement in the technician's voice as well. The letters looked clear, like they were right in front of me. After she left I looked around the room, thinking how much clearer things were since the last time. Dr. Cherne came in and picked up my chart. "This is really great John, you are really coming along. The eye chart is getting easier and easier isn't it?"

"It sure is," I said. "There has been a huge improvement since right before Christmas." We chatted and then he said, "Let's take a look at your eye." I put my face in the slit lamp and Dr. Cherne began a detailed examination. "Your graft is staying very clear, John, it is simply amazing." Then he sat back and turned the light on. "The way you're progressing, John, I truly believe you are going to have 20/20 vision. You will still be legally blind due to the field but it's looking like we hit a home run."

Then it was time for the machine with corrective lenses. Dr. Cherne began to flip lenses and ask if this is better than this or is this better than that. The letters on the eye chart became clearer and clearer. The double vision began to go away, and I knew this was going to be a big improvement. The way I was seeing the eye chart would bring a huge change in my life, even better than the gains during the last five months. Dr. Cherne moved the machine away and said I was doing really well, but it was too soon to take any stitches out. "We still have a lot of healing left to do and we can make the adjustments we need at a later date." He did say that if there were any changes, such as my eyes watering a lot or blurry vision, to call right away. He wanted me to be aware of signs of rejection, although he didn't expect it, but he told me he would see me anytime, night or day.

We set the next appointment for May, and as we walked to the car I was on cloud nine. I knew I had made huge improvements. The difference between reading 20/40 print and seeing it at a distance is huge. Things don't blur into oblivion like it does when the number gets higher in your visual acuity.

On the drive home I was pointing out new things I could see in the afternoon light. Conversation came easily with Anita now. I could point out something to talk about, not rely on her to always carry the conversation. It was neat to be able to look at the paper and direct her attention to something. Anita was always so attentive. We had always been best friends and lovers, but these last five months we had been like newlyweds again. After we arrived home I called both my children and told them the results of my eye tests. I couldn't believe my vision had been returned to me in such a magnificent state.

The next eight days were a whirlwind, getting Holly ready to move to Las Vegas. When everything was packed and loaded she and Cameron would stay with us for two days. Cameron gets severe motion sickness, so he was to fly to Las Vegas with a friend and the rest of us would drive with the family pet.

We set out early on a dull, dreary day and as dawn arrived we were in the Siskiyou Pass. There had been a threat of rain and snow but we made it through the mountains without any problem. At Mount Shasta we headed towards Reno through the mountains, driving through snow for four hours until we got to Susanville, California. The snow continued on and off, never getting above eight inches, but Holly kept her speed between twenty-five and thirty and we moved along with ease.

After Susanville we left the snow for drizzling rain. At Reno we turned east to Fallon, then south on I-95. Holly was frustrated because of the slow driving weather, but we couldn't go any farther than Hawthorne, Nevada, because the next town is Tonapah. It is above 6,000 feet and there would be a lot of snow.

The next day we headed south. It had stopped raining but as we reached the higher elevation there was ice on the road, and semi-trucks and cars off the road that had tried to make it through earlier in the morning. The desert was in full winter mode, with snow on the mountaintops and alongside the road. It was so beautiful we pulled over several times to take pictures. Tonapah had over a foot of snow, and nothing was moving until the skip loaders cleared the roads. The town was snowed in, and the motel lots were full. Holly's SUV made it through, and once on the highway we were heading down and the roads improved. After a while it was open desert to our final destination.

By mid-afternoon Holly was showing us their beautiful new home. The next morning, right on schedule, the moving van arrived and the crew started unloading. Anita and I took over setting up the kitchen, then we started assembling beds and getting ready for the night. After a ten-hour day almost all the boxes had been unpacked and we all collapsed in the living room.

Saturday evening my daughter's friend Kim and my grandson Cameron arrived at the airport and Cole went to get them. Cameron had never seen his new home. He walked around the house and then discovered the swimming pool in the back yard. I asked him what he thought about it.

"Grandpa, I don't know what to think. Everything is so different here."

"Don't worry," I told him, "this will become home. This is a different part of the world than where you come from. The desert is different from the mountains where you lived. You will meet new friends at school and look, you already have a swimming pool and a beautiful home."

"I know, Grandpa, but I am going to miss you."

On Tuesday Holly drove us to Laughlin to meet Anita's cousins. I had not seen them since before I got hurt thirty-one years ago. We had spent a lot of time with them over the years and their kids were about the same age as ours. I really wanted to see them, to connect with the past. When we arrived I could not believe how much they looked like I remembered them. Their hair was a little grayer, like mine, and they had new glasses and yes, there were a few wrinkles where there hadn't been before, but I would have known them anywhere. They looked like they did before, just a little older. It was the first time I had met people from the past that I knew I would recognize. It was a very positive experience for me, to find this familiar link with the past.

That night Anita and I talked about all the events with our children, the drive from Oregon, getting Holly settled in and how wonderful it was to see Phil and Wanda again and catch up on old times. I reached over and we hugged goodnight, not knowing one of the biggest transitions with my sight since the surgery would happen the next morning.

What happened was simply magical. To understand it, you must realize that after being blind for decades there is no "bad" vision. Even if it's not so good, anything at all is good vision. At this point after the surgery my range of vision was a small area roughly the size of a dime down in the very corner, like looking down my nose. When I looked straight ahead there was an area that was fuzzy. Then, as if looking into a frosted mirror, I could see the peninsula of Korea in my distorted vision. But on this morning I awoke and went into the bathroom and turned on the light. I was still half-asleep, but I could tell something was going on with my vision. The light seemed a little more intense. I showered and shaved and then dried off the foggy mirror with my towel. My eyes had adjusted to the light in the room and now the spot that I could see clearly was thirty percent of my vision. The area that had been distorted was moving up towards the top of my eyesight. I wasn't sure what I was seeing, or what it meant. I looked at my fingers and moved them back and forth; I didn't have to raise my head and look down my nose to see them clearly. I was able to see them at the bottom of my visual field. Immediately my mind snapped back to Dr. Cherne's warning that any change in my vision could be a sign of rejection. My heart sank. Was this the beginning of the end? I had lost so much sleep in the past with my thoughts of Dennis Walker and how he lost his sight the second time. Now it might be happening to me. What was I going to do? The change seemed good, but it could have been a turn for the worst. The only thing I knew was I needed to keep a close watch on what I saw and possibly make a dash to Las Vegas and fly home that very day.

I didn't have the heart to tell Anita something was going on, and I wasn't sure it was bad. It didn't seem to be anything but an improvement, but it had never been this drastic before. Anita noticed that something was bothering me, but I told her I must be hungry so we went downstairs for breakfast. As we walked through the casino the machines seemed clearer. I didn't have any pain and my eyes weren't watering — none of the warning signs from Dr. Cherne — but maybe I had missed a warning sign. Was this the beginning of the end?

Inside the restaurant the waitress brought menus and coffee. I picked up the menu and held it at ten inches and yes, I could see it a lot better. The letters were clearer and my field of clear vision was a lot bigger. I knew this looked good, but I decided to wait awhile before I said anything to Anita. She hadn't commented that my eye was watering or that something didn't look right, but she kept looking at me and I am sure she wondered what was the matter.

When our meal arrived I could see the whole plate in my view, and I began to relax. Something this good couldn't be bad. If I was losing my sight things would be getting fuzzy or possibly black from my retina detaching, which was a worry to me. I kept watching Anita as I ate breakfast. She would look at me and then at her plate. She could tell something was not quite right. This lifelong partner knew me better than I knew myself at times.

After breakfast we headed out for a morning walk along the Colorado River. As we walked down the path I could see across the river to the buildings on the other side in Bullhead City, Arizona, but it was so different on this sunny morning. I had a magnificent field of vision, the best since my surgery five months ago, and there was nothing detrimental going on. I began to relax. As the hours went by my field of vision became even less distorted.

After lunch with her cousins Anita and I took another walk along the river, taking in the fresh air and the warm breeze coming off the California desert. We stopped and sat on a bench and looked across the river, just enjoying life. Finally I told her, "Anita there is something going on with my eye."

"Is it a good change?"

"I think so. Do you remember Dr. Cherne warning me about rejection? The change started this morning. I have been watching it but I didn't want you to worry. I want you to look at my eye and tell me if you see anything that hasn't been there before. Discoloration or blood veins sticking out — I don't really know what to look for, but I need you to look closely while we are out here in the sun." Anita did a very close examination of my eye and said everything looked the same. I could see a worried look on her face and I told her I didn't think it was bad. The area that had been distorted was going away and was continuing to go away. It was magical. I could look at something, then look away and when I looked back again it was clearer.

"Surely this isn't rejection then," Anita said.

"I don't think so. Whatever it is, it is huge. It is better than I ever anticipated. Maybe this is God answering our prayers. I am continuing to heal miraculously."

We sat a while longer on the bench and then walked up and down the path before returning to the casino to meet my sister and brother-in-law. We had not seen each other in a long time. I could see my sister more clearly, and as I shook Stan's hand I saw the way his face and twinkling eyes lit up. I knew this couldn't be bad. After talking about old times and catching up I finally told them something was going on with my eye, that things were changing fast. The field of vision was improving almost as we talked. They were concerned but I assured them there was no reason to worry. We had dinner together and later that evening I took another walk along the river to see the changes that had happened that day. And yes, there were still more changes. What I had seen that was distorted in the shape of the Korean Peninsula was gone. It was up in less than a quarter of my visual field. I concentrated on the sunset over the mountains of western California, and I knew that our prayers had been answered. I was healing and I was going to have better sight than I ever imagined possible. That night I told Anita, "I don't know what is happening to me but I know I feel truly blessed."

During the night I awoke at four o'clock and made my way into the bathroom. I turned on the light and looked at myself in the full-length mirror. The whole image of myself and the room that had been distorted was gone. About a third of my vision was very good. Another third was fuzzy and badly out of focus, and the rest was barely useful. Around the edge, much like if you burned the edge of a thirty-five millimeter slide, it was black and crinkled, kind of distorted, with a few small bubbles. It was the biggest change that I would ever undergo with my vision. I sat down on the toilet and tears welled up in my eyes, as I knew this was the fulfillment of Dr. Cherne's prediction that my vision might be 20/20 at the end. I didn't see how it could be possible when he told me, but now I knew I would see better than the entire world could have imagined less than five months ago.

The next day we were meeting my sister and brother-in-law for a day trip to Oatman and Kingman and through a forest of ancient Joshua trees before returning to Holly's home in Las Vegas. As we reached the city we decided to tour the Las Vegas strip and see the grand hotels. We recalled the Wee Kirk O the Heather, the wedding chapel where Anita and I were married. Then the question arose, Do you suppose

It's been a long journey. Thirty-three years later, Anita and I returned to the chapel in Las Vegas where we were married.

it's still there? Anita gave directions and we drove toward old town Las Vegas, and right across the street from the Clark County Courthouse there it sat. Thoughts of the past ran through my head as I turned to look at my beautiful wife and thought of her as that young bride. We parked the car and took pictures before driving on to our daughter's house.

We were to fly home in a few days, and Heidi would meet us in Medford and drive us home. When our plane landed Heidi was there with our car and our granddaughter Shelby. We not only had daughters in two places, we also had grandchildren at each location, which made it extra-special. Shelby is quite the artist and had drawn some new pictures for us. Ever since her grandpa got his sight back she has been responsible for all the artwork in our home.

Chapter 11

Appealing for Treatment

Back at home Friday morning we listened to the telephone messages and made notes to return the calls. Suddenly there was an urgent message from Kathy at Laser Associates in Medford. "John, I need to talk to you right away." Then a second and a third message from her. I knew something was wrong, and it was confirmed as I sorted through the mail. There was a letter from the Veterans Affairs office. My heart was pounding and my hands shook as I opened the letter from the Department of Medical Affairs, Roseburg, Oregon.

February 23, 2000
To: Dermatology Associates of Medford Oregon
Dear Sir or Madam,

This is in response to your request for authorization to provide medical services at VA expense for John Malkow. Removal of tattoo pigmentation is considered to be elective surgery at this time the VA does not authorize non-VA care for elective cosmetic surgery. If you have any questions please contact the fee basis office at (telephone number).
Sincerely,

Patient Accounts Coordinator

I will omit the man's name for he will have to answer someday for his terrible decisions and the veterans that he has condemned. I read the letter several times, then handed it to Anita. She was silent as she sat down and began to read. She knew what this meant. We had been turned down by all the government entities that were supposed to help me. What happened to "Don't worry, buddy, we'll take care of you"? How could the people from Medicare declare it elective surgery and the Department of Defense also refuse to stand behind me? This was a service-connected injury for which I was given a 30% disability, in addition to 100% disability for being blind, 40% for loss of my thumb and 10% for loss of hearing. I could not believe it. I was beside myself. All my trust in the United States government was gone. I wouldn't nor will I ever trust anyone in the government again.

This letter meant this beauty-and-the-beast relationship with my wife and children must go on for the rest of my life. They would have to endure all the ogles and stares. People are not kind in this situation. My mind would skip back to Dr. Cherne telling me, Do you know all of these marks can be removed from your face? Then Dr. Naversen and Dr. Igelman telling me there was help, that it could all be removed. But the decision had been made by a patient accounts coordinator not to spend the money. What my family and I endured didn't mean a damn thing to this bureaucrat. The government had pillaged and taken away my benefits and now they were condemning me to receive no treatment for a service-connected disability. And this was after they had done nothing to help restore my eyesight.

Over the weekend the sting of this latest slap in the face from the United States government eased. It was the same old feeling I had had for thirty-one years. They weren't going to help me and they weren't going to let anyone else help me, either. Still, Dr. Naversen wanted to talk to me, so maybe there was hope. I didn't know how to find help, but as my anger grew I decided to pursue every avenue, from the news media to the Congress, to let people know what was going on. I had been turned down before, but this time I had it in writing.

As my restless Sunday night became Monday morning I finally got up at three-thirty so Anita could get some sleep. I had to come up with a plan, as we could not meet with Dr. Naversen without having some kind of alternative. It was difficult to try to think rationally. I had felt such elation to have my eyesight restored, only to see my disfigured face more clearly. It was even more hideous than it had been before.

We were to meet at Dr. Naversen's office later that morning. Before leaving I got out a copy of my official list of service-connected disabilities. I didn't know what to do but I knew I needed to stay calm and come up with a rational plan.

"John, I do not understand what is going on," Dr. Naversen said as he held up a letter he had received:

> Department of Veteran Affairs
> Roseburg Oregon
> To: Dermatology Associates of Medford
> Dear Sir or madam,
> This is an answer to your request for authorization to provide medical services at VA expense for Mr. John Malkow. Removal of tattooing is considered to be an elective cosmetic surgery. At this time the VA does not authorize non-VA care elective cosmetic surgery. If you have any questions please call our fee basis office at (telephone number).

It was signed by the patient accounts coordinator.

Dr. Naversen looked at me. "This man should not be making these kinds of decisions."

"Dr. Naversen," I told him, "this man does make these decisions and he has been making these decisions for quite some time. He had given my physician such a hard time that I was asked not to return. They simply didn't want to deal with Mr. Patient Accounts Coordinator."

Dr. Naversen told me that he was currently treating a veteran who was having a picture tattoo removed from his upper arm at VA expense. The only difference was that the man moved here from Washington and the Washington office was billed.

It made no sense. Do veterans in Washington get better care than the guys in Oregon? I thought I served in the United States Army. Are VA benefits handed out differently in different states?

"I don't know what to do," he said.

"Dr. Naversen," I said, "I have thought about this all weekend. I have tried to put aside Mr. Patient Accounts Coordinator and the others in Veterans Affairs that let me be blind for thirteen years longer than I had to be and are now denying me treatment for my face. Dr. Naversen, we simply have to have faith in the system. I can't give up hope after all this."

"I would like you to reapply to the system," I told him. "Everyone has to have a boss. Let's write to this patients account coordinator, the bean counter, and mail a copy to his boss, the VA director in Roseburg, and to his boss in Portland. I don't know what is going on any more than you do. All I know is it is not right. I brought a copy of my disabilities certificate that you can include with your letter so they won't have to waste their time looking it up."

Dr. Naversen took the letter and began to read it:

Department of Veteran Affairs
Regional Office Portland
To Whom it may Concern:

This letter is to verify that, according to the records of the United States Veteran Affairs, John C. Malkow has the following service connected disabilities:

Loss of eye and blindness of the other eye 100% disabling
Loss of thumb 40% disabling
Facial scars 30% disabling
Tinnitus 10% disabling
Impaired hearing 0% disabling
Perforated ear drum 0% disabling

If you have any questions call our toll free number

Signed,
Team Leader

"Dr. Naversen," I said, "this time I want you to submit pictures of my face so maybe these people can understand what I must go through daily in life. Surely there is someone up there with a heart."

He could hear the desperation in my heart and voice. "John, we will do it. We will apply to these people like you want and if it comes back denied by God, John I will do you for free and when I am done with you, you will look like a movie star."

With that he turned quickly and left the room. I could tell he was angry, but this wonderful doctor who repairs facial deformities had held his hand out to offer hope, and help. I had been thrown a life ring, and if I had to I would take his offer of help so my family would not endure this anymore.

Shortly after our meeting I received a copy of Dr. Naversen's letter:

Dermatologist and Laser Associates of Medford
March 6, 2000
To: Patient Accounts Coordinator
Department of Veteran Affairs
Roseburg Oregon
Reference: John C. Malkow
Dear Sir,

This letter concerns John C. Malkow, Medicare claim number, who has a service-connected disability. As you may know, he suffered an explosion while on active duty, developing extensive tattoo pigmentation and scars to his face, neck, ears, abdomen, hands, and wrists. This explosion blinded both his eyes and blew off his right thumb.

Mr. Malkow was pretty much resigned to the fact that he would have to live with the disfiguring explosion marks and scars for the duration of his life. However the VersaPulse C laser is now available. This $200,000 state-of-the-art laser is for foreign body tattoos, explosion-related tattoos.

This letter is to get authorization for these needed treatments. The code that would be used best to fit would be 17999, and each visit for a 50 cm square session would be $794.00. Mr. John Malkow would certainly appreciate getting authorization for these sessions, which would total 12 in number. He does not wish to be financially responsible under the circumstances that this was an on the job injury.

This is not a merely a cosmetic problem. This explosion has changed this man's whole life and has made him stand out in a crowd. Why, anyone in the same auditorium with him would be pretty soon staring at him. If this injury was on your skin or one of your children's skin, would you say it was simply cosmetic? I certainly appreciate your consideration. If you have any questions or comments please do not hesitate to contact me.

Please see attached photos.

Sincerely,

Douglas N. Naversen M.D.

With copies to Medical director Hospital Roseburg and team leader Portland as well as John C. Malkow

As I listened to his letter there were tears running down my face. I knew Dr. Naversen had hit a home run, and I asked Anita what she thought. "The pictures should do it. If anyone in their right mind looks at these pictures they could not deny you treatment for what you have coming." That was true, but they had turned me down so many times before I didn't know what to think. I went back to work in my shop and tried to stay busy, as I knew it would take several weeks for the letter to work its way through the bureaucracy.

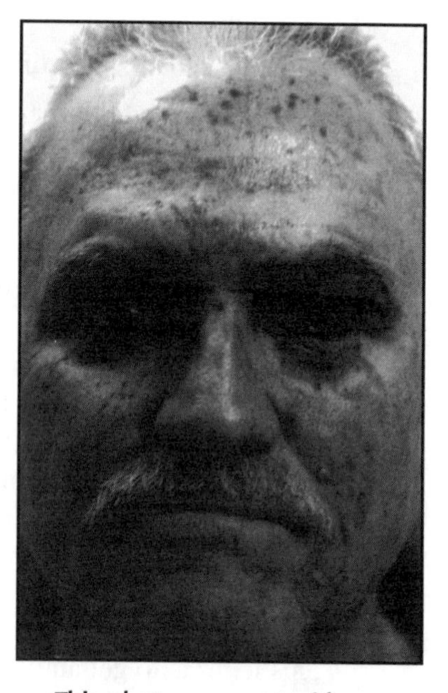

This photo was sent with my appeal

I began to rehabilitate myself again, this time making the adjustments from doing things as a blind person to using my eyesight.

Driving nails, which I had done while blind, was now enormously difficult. My hand, that had been such a good friend all these years, would get in the way. Now that I could see the nail I began to smash my fingers. I would have to start a nail and then put my hand in my pocket. To practice, I wore safety glasses as I drove nails and built small projects. I built a wood box using a tape measure, a luxury that I had not had for thirty-one years. After a few days it became easier and my carpentry began to improve. I was reading the tape right, setting up the saw correctly, and I didn't have to close my eyes so often.

One afternoon an extraordinary thing happened. A windstorm had lifted one of the plastic lift jacks from my old travel trailer that I use on hunting trips. It was laying out in the driveway, and I needed to fix it or it could cause a real problem. So I got up and measured the roof jack and saw the size I needed, went down to the hardware store and got a new one, brought it home and began to put it on the roof. Always before when I was having difficulty with slotted screws I would try to put my fingernail in the slot to find the direction and then put the screwdriver in and make about a quarter turn before it came out. This was the method I had used for over thirty-one years, and the only way I knew to do it. On this job the screws were very long and after about twenty minutes I had one side halfway on and had just started the other side. In a kind of despair I laid my head on my folded arms up there on top of the trailer, trying to regain my composure. I opened my eyes and to my amazement I was looking right at the slot on the troublesome screw. I had never thought to look, to see if I could see the screw. I had lost this over the years. I kept my eye focused on the slot, inserted the screwdriver and in about fifteen seconds I had both screws tightened. After nearly a half hour of complete frustration the job was completed in under a minute. I went around and changed the other side and finished what would have been a frustrating two-hour job in about forty minutes. If I had thought to use my newfound vision it would have been done in about ten minutes.

As spring came and the grass began to grow I found I was able to run a lawnmower effectively. Even when I was blind I had always cut the lawn, but I did it by mowing lengthwise, then back and forth, and then I'd have to get Anita to come out and get the spots I missed. Now I could actually see where the lawnmower was going. I could put the mower wheel on the wheel rut line and go around and around the lawn. It became an activity that I really enjoyed. I mow the lawn nearly every day, simply because I can.

I found solitude in the woods where I had spent so many years either alone or with Anita. It was peaceful and calm. No problems, and no one poking at us or giving us orders. We weren't asking for anything that wasn't rightfully ours. Just life, freedom and what I had fought so hard for. On the days it wasn't raining I began to cut firewood. I could start and run a chain saw and see what I was doing. I wasn't comfortable doing the work before, but with my newfound vision it was a joy. I had two homes to cut for, ours and Heidi's, so we needed quite a woodpile. The only problem was sharpening the saw. I had done this for thirty-one years with my eyes closed, much like driving nails. I used to set it up and hold it just so, swipe the file across and feel with my finger. When I first tried to do it with my eyes open I filed the wrong end of the saw. I would have to educate my eye to go where my fingers should go, in a kind of reverse rehabilitation from blindness to sighted. Some of these things take longer than others to relearn. But it is all God's gift and it will all come in time.

In late March Anita picked up our groceries and mail, including another letter from Veterans Affairs in Roseburg. It had been less than two weeks since Dr. Naversen wrote, and I expected this would be the final determination. We sat down at the dining room table and Anita opened the letter and began to read.

> Dermatology and Laser Associates
> From: Department of Veterans Affairs
> Dear Dr. Naversen:
>
> The request dated February 8, 2000 for authorization to provide medical services to the above named veteran at Department of Veterans Affairs (VA) expense has been reviewed by our medical staff and approved for VersaPulse C laser for removal of tattoo pigmentation on face, neck, ears, abdomen, hands and wrists. If additional services or further treatment are required, a progress report and plan of treatment must by

submitted for consideration by our professional staff and authorized before care is rendered at VA expense.

The physician's report and treatment plan should include:

__ Pertinent history and physical findings
__ Current diagnosis and/or problems
__ Treatment regimen or services required
__ Therapeutic objective
__ Frequency and duration of visits or procedures
__ Estimated cost of treatment
__ Other:

Payment will be made in accordance with the VA Medical Fee Schedule and shall be considered payment in full. Supplemental or duplicate claims for the particular services rendered under this authorization must not be submitted to other parties.

Thank you for your cooperation in the care of this veteran. If you have any questions, please feel free to contact our office by mail or phone.

Sincerely,
Patient Accounts Coordinator

I had been accepted. Dr. Naversen's second letter had somehow been overlooked, or maybe this was to save face. I really didn't care. This was all I needed, the clearance to have my face treated. I hugged Anita and ran to the phone to call Dr. Naversen's office. They hadn't gotten a copy of the letter yet, but the next day Kathy called as soon as the letter arrived and set my first appointment. I was on cloud nine again. I could never understand why you had to hit someone over the head or get a Congressman to force people to do the right thing. Veterans died, lost limbs and eyes, and millions of gallons of blood, and they sit in wheelchairs while the people who make decisions seem not to care at times.

I continued my rehabilitation by sawing firewood and working in my shop to make the transition from blind to sighted, trying to gain proficiency with all the tools I had used for thirty-one years. I enlisted a friend to show me how to fall a tree, for I had several small trees I wanted to remove. When I told Dr. Cherne about it he asked if I wore safety glasses and I assured him that I did, and I could run now too, for I would never have done this when I was blind. The transition from being blind to sighted was coming along well most of the time, but not always. Reading was difficult, as I transposed letters and sometimes words. I didn't know what caused this. It had to be my brain. I knew I was seeing better than my brain thought. After all the travel, dealing with the government and meeting with Dr. Naversen I really needed to unwind. Anita and I needed time by ourselves, just spending time in our woods looking and loving and feeling free.

Two hours before my first facial treatment I got out the packet of cream and applied it to my face. Like a woman would apply cold cream, I smeared on the Lasercaine and rubbed it in around the eye areas. Dr. Naversen had asked where I wanted him to start, and that was the darkest part of all. I had no idea what it would be like, but I knew the cream would help dull the sensation of pain. As we got ready to leave for Medford I got out the ice chest and filled the container and several sandwich bags with ice to reduce the swelling afterwards. The pigment on my face was so severe, it would absorb a lot of the laser energy, as intended. That would set up an inflammation that would prompt the white blood cells to carry the pigmentation to my lymph nodes. I had prayed all night long, and now a calm came over me as I checked my watch and followed the pretreatment instructions to the letter.

When we reached the office Sharon was ready for me. "There is a little more to this than you had anticipated," she told me. "We're going to apply some more cream to your face and cover it in plastic wrap so it doesn't dissolve in the air. This is going to take away a lot of the pain. Then Dr. Naversen will give you an injection that will help calm you and reduce the pain so this will be as comfortable for you as possible."

When the preliminary steps were finished I laid back on the bed and listened to the soft music, trying to relax and stop thinking, My God, what are they going to do to me? There was my mentor again, George Foreman, talking to me. "John, you are not a quitter and this is the first round of the fight. We won the last fight and we will win this fight too, John. Remember from the letter to the VA that this could take up to twelve procedures. Well, John, that is how many rounds there are in a championship fight and I know you are up for it. You can do this, John, by God you can do this. You might have to reach down and grab your bootstraps, but you can do this." As I lay there dreaming of George Foreman's words and anticipating what was to come I began to relax and soon Sharon returned.

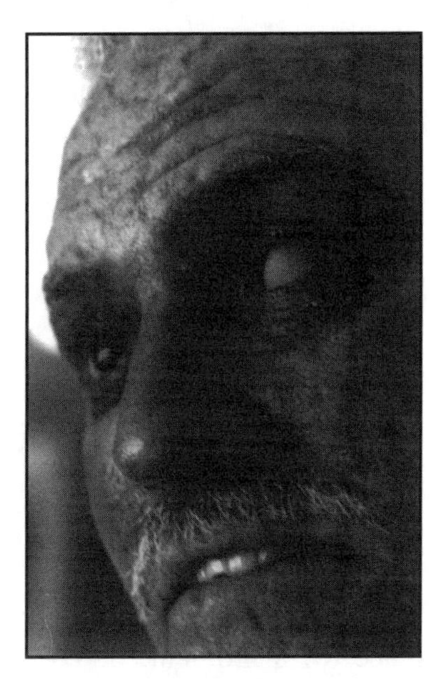

In April 2000, at age fifty-two, I began the series of laser treatments. An eye shield protected my left eye during the treatment.

"John, I want you to sit up. We're going to take you to the treatment room now." I stood up, feeling a little woozy, and grasped her arm. I knew I was in good hands. This was meant to be. As I lay down on the treatment table Sharon raised my head to a comfortable position and pulled out a footrest for my feet. Dr. Naversen came into the room and asked how I felt. I told him I had never felt better in my life.

"What do you mean?"

"This is the beginning of the end," I told him. Dr. Naversen turned to Sharon and told her the settings to use on the laser equipment. Then he put drops in my eye to numb it and put an eye shield in place to protect my eye from the laser rays.

"What can you see?"

"Absolutely nothing."

"That's just what I wanted to hear. You can begin now," he said to Sharon.

I told her I was ready. She touched the trigger and there was a fiery stab, much like a red-hot needle. Then another, and another, and the laser began to TICK, TICK, TICK. As it stabbed and stabbed and stabbed I tried to put myself in the place I have for pain. It's a coping mechanism that a lot of people use for pain.

"How are you doing?" Sharon asked.

"Very well," I replied as she made a pattern across my forehead. "This is not a bad pain. This is a good pain." The darker the pigment, the more the laser works and the more your body absorbs it. STAB, STAB, STAB. Dr. Naversen also checked on me.

"I'm doing fine," I told him, but I really wasn't doing fine. Then my friend George was back. "John, get ahold of yourself. I told you this was the first round. You will have to get hold of yourself by your bootstraps. I know this hurts, but we have twelve rounds to go. We have to be ready." Back inside the place I have for pain it wasn't so bad; it was being masked. I held it back there as the stabs moved down around my eyes and over the top of my left eye. BANG, BANG, BANG. Then around my eyelid. BANG, BANG, BANG. Kathy came in and rubbed my shoulder and asked how I was doing. I told her I was fine. She took me away from my place for a moment. BANG, BANG, BANG. Then Dr. Naversen was asking, "If there was a scale from one to ten what would the pain be?"

"A three, Doctor." And I meant it. I had been hurt more with words than physical pain could ever do to me. I was trying to think of anything but the TICK, TICK, TICK of the laser. I said to Kathy and Sharon, "You know, there just might be a prince under all of this." Then I found a place to go, back in time, as where I was in the present wasn't acceptable. I began to relate stories from the past. I told them about the policeman years ago, telling me, in front of my wife, that I should wash my face before I came to town. And the woman in the store who told her child that I was what a nigger looked like. I could not believe that anyone could have this attitude, and even worse, to teach it to their children. But it had been done to me and was still being done. Things hadn't changed all that much. Again came the fiery STAB, STAB, STAB and TICK, TICK, TICK of the laser. Suddenly the idea came. John, this is a magic wand. This is the thing that will relieve you of all your pain, and when this is over, just like in the fairy tales, there will be happiness ever after.

Soon Sharon reached down and rubbed my shoulder as Kathy rubbed the other shoulder. "John, we're finished."

"Thank God." I felt like I had been put through the works, but it was really more mental than physical. It hurt, but it was well worth the hurt and I knew this would not be the last of it. From the first facial surgery I had back in the 1970s, it all hurt but it was all worth it.

Anita came in and helped me out of the room. Sharon and Kathy and advised me to use ice right away, because my face would really swell up. When we reached the car I put two big bags of ice on my forehead and over my eyes. I knew soon I was going to look like George Foreman himself had beaten me, and sure enough, by the time we arrived home an hour later I could not see out of my eye. I relied on Anita to lead me into bed, and the shot Dr. Naversen had given me would take away the pain for some time. The pain is only during the procedure, and it is easy after awhile. You have to remove yourself. It is a mental process, and people with facial deformities are more than willing to endure the pain to get results.

Sharon called that evening to check on me. She knew my eyes were swollen after what I had gone through that day. I told her I was in good shape and for a lady of about 120 pounds she packed a fearful punch. I had to use my fingers and spread my eye apart to see anything at all. "Isn't this great?" I said.

"I'm so happy to help you, John, I really feel happy."

The next day my eyes were pretty much swollen shut. By the second day they became slits and I didn't have to hold my eyes open with my fingers anymore. I could kind of stretch my face and be able to see, and I was alternating ice and hot compresses and applying antibiotic ointment to guard against infection as Dr. Naversen had ordered. By the third day the swelling was almost gone and I began to do close examinations in the mirror every morning, just as close as I could get, to see if the tattooing was going away. I could see a difference. It began to disappear in very small spots on my forehead, and the darkest spot under my right eye had grown smaller. It was not as much as I expected, and I knew it would take a lot more treatments but I was willing to endure it, as I knew after each treatment it would be lighter and lighter.

As soon as I was able I was back outside, mowing the lawn almost every day. I also worked in my shop to rehabilitate my hands. My hand-eye coordination wasn't as good as it used to be. I had never missed my right eye before, but now it appeared that I would have problems with depth perception. This is common for people who have only one eye, as depth perception requires two eyes. This was apparent while I was driving nails. I knew where I wanted to hit, but the strike would be either short or long. I knew I would have to work hard to overcome this problem and it has gradually lessened.

By the first of May it was time for another laser treatment. I was optimistic, as I knew we were making strides. I had looked in the mirror every day and I knew the scarring was lessening. On the morning of the procedure I rubbed the cream on again and this time I applied it to my cheeks and chin and neck as well as my forehead and around my eyes.

At the clinic we again started with the pain medication. Then I was ushered into the treatment room where Sharon was getting things ready. Dr. Naversen came in and said, "Hi John, let's see how we did." He held up the pictures taken in January, and he and Sharon both could see progress. Dr. Naversen seemed very happy. He told me this would not go away immediately. I would have to have several treatments but he could see a difference already. Then he put my eye to sleep and inserted the eye shield and gave Sharon the directions for setting the laser. She started to work on my forehead and again the fiery stab of the laser's TICK, TICK, TICK began. I immediately put myself in the place I have for pain and soon the treatment was over. This time the procedure had been done not only on my eyes but also on my forehead, nose, cheeks, neck and ears. At the end of the treatment my old buddy George was back. He was proud of me this time. "This was the second round and it went easier didn't it?"

"Yes George, it did," I said to myself.

"Well John, each round is going to get easier now. It's going to go away. We're going to win this one too."

I have found it very helpful to have a mentor's help in a time of trouble, and I had chosen a wonderful mentor. Someone who thinks kindly of other people and is tough, mentally as well as physically. And with God overseeing it all, there was no way I could lose.

Anita again came to help me to the car, and I put ice on my face for the long ride home. We talked about the treatment and I told Anita it felt less severe this time. Maybe I was mentally more prepared this time, or maybe the pigment wasn't diffusing as much as it did the first time. To Anita it seemed like a lot to go through, but it was worth every bit of it. I told her one of these days she would get back the man she married over thirty-two years ago.

I stayed in bed and kept ice on my face for the remainder of the day. My eyes were swollen shut again, and I had to hold my eye open to make my way to the table for dinner. I ate with one hand and held my eye open with the other. I guess I could have let my eye stay closed and gone back to eating like I did when I was blind, but somehow I couldn't let myself do that. I want to see everything I can, every minute of the day.

I went to bed early that night and fell right asleep. I awoke at my usual eleven and three and arose at four o'clock, all ready for the day. I made my way to the front bathroom to start my hot compresses to promote healing. It felt good to put those hot, steamy compresses on my face. It was very relaxing to feel the warmth go into my face.

By breakfast time the swelling had gone down enough that I could see to get around. That had taken two days after the first treatment, so this was an improvement. Then I began the routine of looking in the mirror four or five times daily. Turning on the light and getting as close as I could to the mirror looking, searching to find a spot that wasn't there anymore or a large stain that was just a bit lighter. Someday it would be totally gone, and I could not wait for the day I could take this face off and see what I really looked like.

May 2000 was beautiful, as always. It is very pleasant as the weather warms and the days lengthen out. I had a big job to do. I didn't have enough firewood cut for our house and Heidi's house for the winter, so I began to work in the woods every day. This was such a joy, such a relief to me. Our property began to look like a park as I took out trees and trimmed the limbs. The piles of firewood grew larger and larger, and finally there was enough. But I kept going for the peace and serenity this gave me, and the time that I needed for my eye to heal and my mental state to be calmed as I watched my face getting better. There was no one to talk to at this time. There was no one who had been blind for thirty-one years and got their sight back that I could talk to, and no one who had facial disfigurements removed after thirty years that I could talk to. I went through this process by myself, just like the years of blindness and my rehabilitation afterwards. If it hadn't been for my family I don't know what I would have done. They mean so much to me.

Chapter 12

Giving Back, Looking Back

One day I got a call from Lynn Rardin, Dr. Cherne's assistant, about an event that turned out to be the most wonderful thing that I could possibly imagine. I finally got to give something back to this wonderful man.

Lynn asked me to attend the dedication of their new office and surgery center in Eugene. She said Dr. You and Dr. Cherne were so proud of me that they wanted to show people the results of this miraculous surgery. There would be local dignitaries and invited guests as well as some of the investors in the building. I told her it would be an honor and a privilege, so we rescheduled my appointment for May 17; the dedication would be at six-thirty that evening.

When we arrived at the Clear Vision Institute that day, everyone was busy with preparations. As we waited I became interested in the large aquarium. It was the first fish tank I had ever seen, and the colors were simply gorgeous. It had blue sand and iridescent blue and white fish and orange fish with long white stripes swimming through the bubbles. When I moved closer they seemed to get interested in me and swam closer to the glass. What a view.

When the time came for the eye chart the results were just like the last time. I could read the largest letters, but I stopped at the 20/80 line. With the partial cover I read at the 20/40 line but strained at the 20/30 line. It was just too fuzzy. "Someday, John, someday," the technician assured me. Then Dr. Cydel came in to let me know that Dr. Cherne was delayed in surgery and would see me tomorrow instead. Meanwhile, Dr. Cydel asked if he could examine me so I moved up to the slit lamp and he began his examination.

"This is truly a miracle, John. I would never have believed this would be possible."

He finished the examination and then brought up the instrument with test lenses. Things looked fuzzy as he began to flip the lenses. "Is this better than this?" "Is this better than this?" I would answer and he would change the lens and ask again. Finally there it was — the eye chart was clear and only slightly out of focus. I wasn't seeing double, and oh, how I didn't want this to end. I wanted to take the machine with me and look through it for the rest of my life. Dr. Cydel told me my eye was stable, exactly the same as it had been in February. He said Dr. Cherne might want to make some adjustments when he saw me the next day.

Anita and I drove to the hotel and checked in. We got to our room and I went to open the curtains to let in some light. Suddenly we were looking at the most majestic view of the Willamette River one could imagine. The scene was simply breathtaking through the trees overlooking a beautiful picnic area above the river. Anita and I sat out on the deck and took in the beautiful view and watched the sunset until it was time to get ready for the dedication.

Back at the Clear Vision Institute we joined a crowd of eighty to a hundred, including the news media, local officials and Congressional representatives. After the introductions Dr. Cherne came back to the podium. "I would like all of you to close your eyes for a minute." After the pause he said, "You can open your eyes now. We have a visiting guest here, a man that Dr. You and I have both treated. You were only blind for a minute, but he was blind for over thirty years and now he sees. We would like to welcome him to this dedication." Everyone began to applaud as I made my way forward. My message was brief: my lasting gratitude for the work these doctors do. I took my place between Dr. You and Dr. Cherne and as the staff was introduced I took out a paper that I had drawn of what my vision was like before that day along the Colorado River. With the distortion my vision had been shaped like the peninsula of Korea. I leaned over to Dr. You and asked him what would cause this. He looked back with a huge grin. "John, that is your retina. I have never seen anyone like you." Then he patted me on the arm. Dr. Cherne leaned over and I showed it to him and he shook his head and patted me on the other shoulder. People in the audience probably thought it was a model of a new car or some exotic photo, but it was strictly business. It was the first time I had seen my doctors since February, and I simply could not hold the good news. Then it was time for the ribbon cutting and tours of the new facility. I could hardly believe what I saw — all the cutting-edge technology and equipment. It was like a dream come true to someone who has been blind. As Anita and I walked around we met Lynn and thanked her for providing such a beautiful room. She wiped a tear from her eye and said, "We wanted you to have a view."

The next morning Dr. Cherne asked about the map I had drawn of the Korean Peninsula that had suddenly disappeared from my field of vision.

"This just happened spontaneously?"

"Within twenty-four hours, Doctor, it was gone."

"This is truly remarkable, John. I want to see in your eye." He moved the slit lamp into place and when he came to the corneal transplant he said my graft was crystal clear. This was what I had waited to hear. I knew it was for the better, and I had made the right decision on the Colorado River. Then Dr. Cherne did another topography. As the computer began to spit out a picture of my eye he said, "Your vision is probably good enough to see this now." He pointed out two orange areas on each side of my cornea transplant, then a green area above and below my eye.

"Do you see the green area there? That is forming a natural bifocal for you. That is why you are able to read. These two orange areas mean things are too tight. I could give you glasses now but they would be too thick. Now I think it is time to take out a couple of stitches. We'll take a stitch out on each side and your eye will become round, like a basketball. We may have to do another stitch or two in the future, but this looks pretty good from what I can see."

"When I take these stitches out," he warned me, "it is going to take that bifocal away and you won't be able to read like you have in the past. Things from thirteen inches to about three feet will become clear, and your distance vision will become clearer, but things close to you will become fuzzy. This area from thirteen inches to three feet is our primary area of vision. I have to try to focus your vision at that point."

He had me lean back and put two more numbing drops into my eye and went to get the tiny scissors and other instruments he would need to remove the sutures. "John, this is going to take a little getting used to," he said. "You have been used to the way you see things, but that is going to change."

It was all part of the healing process, I knew. We chatted, and I told him how my rehabilitation had been coming along. Then I wanted to ask a question. I knew my prosthetic eye was not right. It was too big, and the wrong color. It was a real eyesore, Dr. Cherne agreed. "Your eye is too thick and it needs to be painted a different color." I asked him about the new prosthetic eyes that could be attached to the muscles to track like a normal eye. "Can you give me one, doctor? Can you help me with that too?"

He thought for a moment. "John, that is not my specialty. An ophthalmologist doesn't do everything anymore. This is for an orbital doctor, and it would be worth a look. Maybe you could go talk to one, but you had a severe injury, and there's no telling what your muscles look like. Some may have been removed and the old implant is still there and functioning. I don't feel you would be served by having one of these eyes put in. They may not be able to find the muscles. They may be scarred so badly that you could wind up in worse shape than you are now. I feel that you would be best served by getting a new prosthetic eye — one that fits better. A better design, thinner, and painted a better color. I don't think movement is what you are after. It is simply color."

I thanked Dr. Cherne for his honesty and said I would approach the VA about having a new prosthetic eye made. Then he added, "By the way, your face looks somewhat lighter. They've begun work on it, haven't they?"

I had been waiting for this during the entire visit. Dr. Cherne had noticed. “Yes Doctor, I have had two treatments and I am due to have one next week.”

“Well, it’s working, John. I can tell a difference.”

He wanted to see me in six weeks to check my vision after the removal of the sutures. Anita and I made the appointment and walked outdoors into the sunlight. Immediately things were fuzzy. Objects far away seemed clearer, but things in the intermediate range and close up were fuzzy. Things from thirteen inches to three feet were very clear. In the car the emblem on the dashboard was very clear. I held my hand up and it was fuzzy. When I looked across the street the buildings were now clear. That morning they had been fuzzy. I turned to Anita. “This is going to take some real getting used to. I hope my brain will adapt.”

On the drive home things in the distance seemed closer and very clear. My distance vision had definitely improved. I could see the dashboard of the car but when I looked at my watch I had to move it to a different reading area. It was only a process of focus, holding things at a different focal point, not like a miser trying to see the inscriptions on every coin in his sack.

For the next few days I must have looked like someone trying to learn how to play the trombone. I moved the newspaper in and out, and cans and packages in and out, in and out, until I could find the focal point where I could read them.

That May I had been asked to speak at the Lions convention in Ashland. I eagerly agreed to help, and I had volunteered my whole family as well, my wife and both my daughters. Holly and her family were flying back from Las Vegas to attend the function.

I was struggling to figure out what people would want to hear. Did they want to know what it was like to be blind and get your sight back, or the experience at the moment of getting your sight back, or the things I had done since then? I spent two days making notes, as I was to be the featured speaker at the 2000 Oregon Lions convention. It was an honor and a privilege, but I labored over what to say. I had rehearsed and rewritten my speech many times. It sounded good to me but I hadn't tried it on anyone else.

When Holly, Cole and Cameron arrived Heidi joined us for a family barbecue. Later that evening Heidi asked me, "Dad, what do you want us to say?"

"I want you to say exactly what is in your heart. You and Holly both need to tell people what this has meant to you."

"There aren't words for that, Dad," Heidi said. I reminded her that the Lions were the reason I can see. The gift of my cornea came from the Lions. They help people with hearing aids, corneas, glasses and many other things. "Heidi," I said, "you and I are both Lions and you know what that means."

Then Holly asked, "Dad, do you want us to tell what it was like when you were blind or now that you can see?"

I didn't really know, I said, but I was sure that our story would help people. I would be able to thank all the Lions at the state convention, on behalf of every recipient, for all the work they had done, not in a letter but in person. The Lions could actually see the results of their work and their financial contributions.

At the last moment before leaving the house I went back to the bedroom and got out one of my most valued possessions — the letter from the wife of the young man who had been my donor. It had been given to me by the Lions through Marshal Santos. The recipient and the donor's family can communicate through the eye bank to maintain strict privacy. I put the letter in the pocket with my speech as we left the house.

We arrived at the convention, where the meeting opened with introductions and a speech by the state Lions president. Then the president of the eye bank spoke, thanking those who had helped the eye bank and given corneas for their successful efforts. Then it was my turn and I took the podium. I took out my speech and began to read some of my notes. As I spoke I looked around and saw that people were wiping their eyes. I was talking faster than I could read my notes, and the things that I had written were not coming out of my mouth. I soon set my notes aside and for the next twenty minutes I told my story. The force of the explosion, like an atomic bomb. Learning to live as a blind person. Seeing

Dr. You's watch after the surgery, then seeing my wife and daughters for the first time. What I had done for rehabilitation and how I had become a Lion myself. I looked around and again saw people wiping their eyes. The international director of the Lions organization reached into his pocket for a handkerchief and began to wipe his eyes. As my speech ended a calm came over me. I took out the letter from the donor's family to read a portion of it so the Lions would know what it was like to be in the position of giving permission to harvest the organs of a loved one. I began to read this wonderful woman's very touching letter and when I finished there wasn't a dry eye in the place. I had helped them all to understand what it was like to receive the gift of sight and what it felt like to the family of a donor. As Lions, I told them, I know you have all carried corneas to the eye bank, and at two o'clock in the morning it is not always convenient. But the next time you get a call, I said in closing, I want you to remember me and then I would like you to remember the wonderful young lady who gave this gift.

I received a standing ovation. The International Lions director, who was seated next to me, stood up and hugged me and told me what an inspiration I was to them all. I then turned to my family. Anita and Heidi were too moved by my speech to talk but Holly, as usual, pulled it together and joined me on the podium. She talked about what it was like to have a blind father, and how she grew up not feeling different from other kids. How I had participated with them in all their activities and how their friends never looked at me as blind, just Heidi and Holly's dad. Then seeing me doing things that I had not been able to do before, and how our property looked more like a park than a forest. Holly closed by thanking the Lions for all they had done for our family as well as for other people in Oregon.

Afterwards we spoke with several people in the lobby, including a member of the Lions who asked if she could speak to Holly. She explained that she could only see light out of one eye because of a degenerative disease, and she was concerned about what her nine-year-old daughter, whom she had never seen, and her daughter's friends would think of her. It had been on her mind like it had been on my mind for thirty years, and she was so relieved to learn that my daughters had grown up with a normal life. Holly and Heidi both assured her that I was no different from any of their friends' dads. I simply did things differently. The lady stopped sobbing and began to smile and we could see the relief come over her. If there was anything we wanted to accomplish at this convention it was this: to thank the Lions and to help other people like this beautiful woman.

Back at home I began to prepare for another family barbecue. Holly and Cole would be going out to celebrate their wedding anniversary, so it was Cameron, Shelby, Heidi, Anita and I for dinner.

The next morning Cole, Cameron and I were to play golf. It would be my first golf game since I was in high school, and I had purchased a starter set of clubs, shoes, balls and all the paraphernalia. My eight-year-old grandson had golf clubs, and Cole had his. We all made our way to the first tee box and Cole hit a big slice that landed out of bounds. I was next, and after a couple of practice swings I also hit the ball and then hit the ball out of bounds. We moved to the junior tee where Cameron teed up and hit the ball straight as an arrow about 85 yards. I was thrilled to see my grandson do so well.

"Are you going to be the next Tiger Woods?" He smiled at me. "I don't know, Grandpa, but I sure like this." Finally on the third tee I hit the ball right down the fairway. After Cole and Cameron teed off Cole pointed out my ball. I had hit it nearly 200 yards, and straight. I knew I would be able to play this game and it would be an excellent exercise for my hand-eye coordination. We played the rest of the day, and each good shot was inspirational. I was amazed that I could do that well. There were a lot of bad shots, but being a very competitive person I knew I would improve with practice. Now I have an electric putting machine in my living room and Anita and I practice constantly and play every chance we get. Both of our daughters have taken up golf also, so it's become a family event.

I had been looking for a general physician to take Dr. Tanczos's place when Anita saw an article in the newspaper about one of our former 4-H kids who is now a nurse practitioner. Ray Millette had been one of my favorite students. I met him when he was starting the seventh grade, and now he was thirty-one and a nurse practitioner.

Ray had done very well in high school and then joined the military and married his high school sweetheart. He had been in the Army medical corps like I had and then went to nursing school and became a nurse practitioner.

"Ray is going to be my new doctor," I told Anita. "I can't think of a better person." The next day I called and made an appointment to see him on his very first day in business.

When Ray came into the examination room he hugged me. "I can't believe what has happened to you."

"Well," I said, "I can't believe what has happened to you, Ray. You have grown from that scrawny little kid in 4-H into a young man with a family of your own." He told me about his two little boys, seven and nine years old, and asked about my life. Then he told me that when he had seen my name on his first patient list he had wept to see that I was there to help him again.

"You probably forgot, but when I was a kid I came to your house looking for a hog to get started in 4-H. My dad was between jobs and things were tough. You were selling pigs for forty-five dollars at the time. You knew I really wanted to be in 4-H and when I looked at one and asked how much it cost you said 'Well how much have you got, Ray?' I had fifteen dollars in my pocket and you said 'Well, I guess that hog is fifteen bucks.' John, I never forgot that."

I told Ray I planed on getting that thirty bucks for the rest of our lives, that he was going to be my doctor and take care of me until either he quit or I died. We shook hands on that pact and Ray began his examination. He told me I was still in excellent health and to continue my diet and exercise, especially my thirty minutes every day on the bicycle.

Over the next few days I began to notice a change in my eyes again. The perspective began to improve, and things were shaped correctly, not flat or crescent-shaped. My ability to read had lessened but I could still do so with concentration. The area between thirteen inches and three feet was reasonably good and my distance vision was getting better. I could pick out individual trees and identify them. With magnification or bifocals I would have close-up vision again.

Holly was due to return to pick up Cameron. We had enjoyed our time together very much, and he had lots of adventures to share with his mother. Holly had been working on this book, and now she wanted to go through our family pictures and get photos to go with the story. I told her that I had reservations about looking through photos. Going back into the past had been very difficult for me at times. Christmas was a very emotional time for me.

"I know, Dad, but we really have to do this," Holly said, so I said I would prepare myself and first thing tomorrow we would get out the photos.

That night as I lay there waiting for sleep I hoped the next day would not be as rough as Christmas had been. Maybe it was just the season, but I didn't think so. They had taken lots of pictures through the years — a complete chest of drawers full of pictures. This would not be just a few minutes; it would take hours, and it could be very grueling. I tried to prepare myself mentally. You have to look at your past, John, I thought as I drifted off to sleep.

The next morning I was up early, drinking coffee, when Anita came into the living room. She hadn't been able to sleep either.

"I hope this isn't too hard on you, John."

"I simply have to face it, Anita," I said. "I have walked into that bedroom so many times and looked at that chest of drawers and thought, I don't know how I am going to do this. I have to do it somehow."

After breakfast I brought out the first drawer of photos and Holly began to arrange them on the kitchen table. As I sat down and she began to hand me photos, much to my dismay there was absolutely no emotion. Nothing. The pictures were from the time I lost my sight until I regained my sight, but there was nothing there. No emotion, no feeling. There were pictures of my mother I did not recognize. I didn't even know what my own mother looked like through the years. I could recognize pictures from when I could see, before I was twenty-one years old. I picked those photos out immediately, but I could only guess at pictures of my children. I couldn't tell the difference between my oldest daughter and Anita. I couldn't distinguish pictures of my granddaughter from photos of Anita or my oldest daughter. It was amazing. I thought, My God, what have you done to yourself? You have steeled your emotions until you have no feeling. This can't be, John. You simply can't do this to yourself.

Holly began to arrange photos on the table. "This was me as a child and this was Heidi." The years would go ahead and she would say, "This is me, Dad, and this is Heidi and this is Grandma and this is your mother." As she held up pictures it was like I was in your home, looking at your family photos. They were nice and there were people there, but I had no feeling and I could not understand why. After three or four hours we had gone through all the photos and made the selections. We were going to have dinner later with Heidi and have her look at them too. I was quiet all afternoon; it was very puzzling. I had been so emotional at Christmas but this was different. These were photos that my children had picked out and put in order. I knew who the people were. Heidi had looked so much like her mother, but as they grew older they began to look different. Then the picture of Anita and me at our wedding, the wonderful Christmas gift, and now there was nothing.

Heidi came over after work to look through the photos with us. She liked the selections we had made. Then she looked at me and asked what I thought. I told her I really didn't know what to think. I had steeled myself to where I didn't know if I was looking at my family or someone else's family. There was no emotion, no feeling for these pictures, and I couldn't understand why. Then Heidi said, "Dad, I think I know what's wrong. I think it is like reading a book, when you picture what went on in the book and then they make a movie out of it and it's not what you had pictured in your mind. You have imagined these events and have made mental pictures of what things were supposed to be for the last thirty-one years, and now you look at the pictures and they don't fit with what you had in your mind." Immediately I felt a huge relief.

That was exactly how I had felt, but I didn't understand it until my oldest daughter explained my emotions to me. I was so relieved, as the events in my life meant so much to me and I could not understand how I could not have any feeling. But the people in my life were not how I had mentally pictured them. I didn't recognize them, now that I could see them for real. If I wanted to go back to the past and see things, I would have to close my eyes and go back to being blind.

Chapter 13

Expanding Horizons

As I looked across the lush green Willamette Valley, the fields of grain and grass were like a sea of green and the crops were at their peak. Looking eastward to the foothills of the Cascade Mountains and then west toward the Coast Range, I knew the vision trade-off I had made was well worth it. I would gladly carry a magnifying glass in my pocket for the rest of my life to see something small in exchange for this panoramic view.

It was late June, and Anita and I were driving to Eugene for a follow-up eye appointment. It had been six weeks since Dr. Cherne had removed the stitches from my eye, and there had been a significant change in my vision. My distance vision was much better, and my ability to read street signs was almost double what it had been. I thought about all the trips we had made in the past, and all the changes I had been through. For the first three or four weeks after the cornea transplant surgery I had had waves of nausea and motion sickness on these car trips. Then things would seem to fly by, too blurry to see any detail in the highway signs. Later, things didn't seem to move as fast but I still couldn't read the highway signs. The words seemed to have two or sometimes three images of every letter. Today, though, I looked to my left and saw my beautiful wife, and saw the graying beauty of this wonderful woman who had been my partner for thirty-two years. I felt so blessed. Even if things never got any better than they were right now I would be eternally thankful. My vision had improved by about a third over the last six weeks. Off in the distance I was seeing things that used to blur into oblivion. It was unbelievable to look out across the horizon and see clearly what was only a blur before. Dr. Cherne had warned that this would be an adjustment, but the change was all for the better.

Later that morning, Dr. Cherne and I talked about the changes I had observed and what today's eye test and topographical map had revealed.

"You told me last time this would take some getting used to, and it did," I said. "My focal points changed and I am beginning to get used to it, but it has taken some time. Close-up reading is difficult, and I can't see as much of the small print as I could before. Things in the distance are much clearer and just exactly like you said, things that are in the range of thirteen inches to three feet are reasonably clear," I told Dr. Cherne. "I have no trouble with anything other than when I hit a golf ball there is an enormous slice. Doctor, do you think there is an adjustment in my eye you can make to take care of that?"

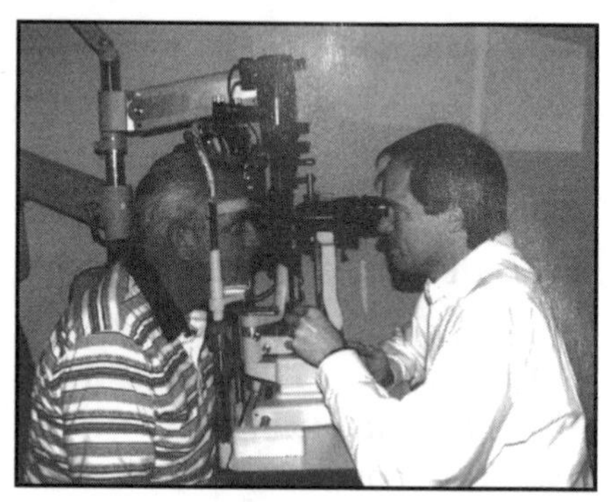

Dr. Scott Cherne delivers the good news. The cornea is clear and my vision continues to improve.

He laughed. "John, they haven't invented a pair of glasses that would fix that yet." Then he said, "They've been working on your face and it is really looking good. The first thing I noticed was how much the dark color around your eye had lessened. So much of the pigment is gone or lighter than before. They are doing a wonderful job."

"It is kind of painful but well worth it," I told him. Then I put my face into the slit lamp and Dr. Cherne began his microscopic exam, relating the results to the technician. When he came to the part that my graft was clear I loved hearing those words. Rejection is the only fear a cornea recipient has.

When he finished Dr. Cherne moved the lens machine into position and asked me to look through various lenses. "Is this better than that one? Is this better?" Then he moved the machine away. "Your vision is still changing," he said. "It's not time yet for glasses. Your vision will change some more. We'll check it again in six weeks and do another topographical map of your cornea to see if it's where it wants to be."

Then Dr. Cherne sat back in his chair and laced his fingers together behind his head. "What have you been up to lately, John?" I told him about my grandson's visit and my first game of golf.

"I kind of wondered where you got the 'slice' in the golf ball."

"Golf has been a Godsend," I told him. "It's a pressure release for me. I don't get angry, I just try harder. And, being a competitive person, I think this will keep me active."

"It's a wonderful thing for your hand-eye coordination," Dr. Cherne said. "Just don't expect too much from yourself."

"I would amaze you, Doctor," I said. "I did better than I thought I could do."

Dr. Cherne asked what was the worst part of getting my sight back. Without a doubt, I told him, it was the loss of sleep. At first I had been plagued with the fear that I could not see anymore. Then he revealed that he had once been in a similar position and would wake up in that same anxious state, heart pounding and gasping for breath. Instantly I felt a kinship, knowing that he could relate to what I was going through and realizing that I wasn't the only person who had experienced something like this.

On our ride home I felt a huge relief. Everyone in the office had noticed the results of the treatments on my face. My appearance was improving, and as a result I became more outgoing. I no longer had to hide my face. It was still dark under my eyes but the rest of my face simply had a gray appearance and even that was lighter with each treatment. It felt like a huge weight had been lifted off my shoulders.

The next day was the first of July and Anita's fifty-sixth birthday, and we planned to celebrate with a family barbecue. Heidi and Shelby came over that evening, and as we ate the corn on the cob, barbecued chicken and sweet beans that Anita had made I looked at my family. My lovely wife of thirty-two years, my oldest daughter and my granddaughter looked like three peas in a pod. I had missed seeing my daughters as young girls, but at that moment I realized that I could recapture my daughters' growing-up years through my granddaughter Shelby. Heidi looked like I remembered Anita in her younger days, and Shelby was a copy of her mother and grandmother. This was a gift that I would appreciate for the rest of my life.

The conversation turned to plans for the Fourth of July. It was to be a marathon event, beginning with a game of golf with the whole family, then after lunch we'd go to the fairgrounds and watch the horse races. Our family had enjoyed horse racing through the years. My mother-in-law Madge would go to the horse races with us two or three times a season, and my daughters grew up watching the horses run. This would be the first time I had seen a horse race since I was twenty years old.

After our golf game on July Fourth we went on to the fairgrounds and had hot dogs while we read over the program, looking at the names of the horses to make our first bet.

Then it was post time and the horses were paraded out. It was a majestic sight, one that I had imagined for so many years, and now they were right in front of me. I used to make my bets simply by the horse's name. Now I actually got to look at the horses and the jockeys and all the pageantry. Then the bugle sounded and the horses headed for the post. The gate was dropped and the horses raced down the track. It was a quarter horse race, only 450 yards, and as those beautiful horses came running by the crowd roared. I was caught up in the excitement, yelling and waving my hat as my horse came in second. What an experience. We had a wonderful day together, but rather than stay to watch the local fireworks I really wanted to go home and watch the fireworks on TV. I wanted to see the fireworks at New York harbor, and then follow them across the country. I hadn't seen fireworks since July 1968, in San Antonio, Texas, when I was going to 91C school.

For two hours I watched, beginning with the spectacular Statue of Liberty and New York harbor, then fireworks displays from all across the country. Later than normal I turned off the TV and went to bed. It had been a wonderful day and a great Fourth of July. It has a special place in my memory.

The next day I was due to have another treatment on my face. Anita and I drove to the clinic in Medford, where I was ushered into the treatment room and given an injection to relax me and help with the pain. After the cream was applied Dr. Naversen came in, very pleased with the improvement. He compared photos of my face, as he had done in the past.

"John, it gets two shades lighter every time we do this. It is really quite noticeable now." I agreed, and told him that Dr. Cherne and his staff had noticed a difference.

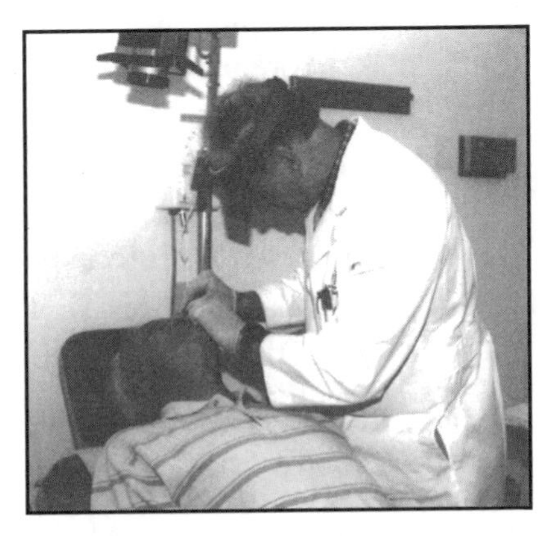

Dr. Douglas Naversen places a shield over my left eye before each laser treatment.

"It's becoming quite apparent that the pigment is leaving, and it's not nearly as severe."

"People don't stare at me like they did before," I told him. "It is still dark around my eyes, but most of the time I have to wear sunglasses due to the sensitivity of my eye. It feels like a huge weight has been lifted from my shoulders, Dr. Naversen."

"John, we're going to continue this until it is all gone." He explained that they were going to use two different lasers on my face today. After going over my face with the bigger one they would use a smaller laser for very small particles. This would be the procedure for the remainder of my treatments.

Dr. Naversen left me in the room alone to prepare myself while the painkiller took effect. I tried to imagine what this would be like. I had only had one laser before and now they were going to use two, so the treatment would be twice as long. Would I have the stamina for it? I knew I would. I would have to gather myself and call on my good buddy George Foreman to help me one more time.

Soon Sharon was back and asked if I was ready. I told her I was, and she began on my left cheek. The laser's methodical TICK TICK TICK sent stabs of fire across my face — around my lips, my nose, then on my right cheek, down to my chin and onto my neck. Then she began working on my right hand. She did my four fingers and then moved up to where my thumb had been. When she touched that black, scarred stump with the laser it was all I could do to hold it there. It was extremely painful. I reached over with my other hand and grabbed my wrist and held my hand down so Sharon could do her work. Then she said "John, let me see your other hand." She touched my forearm and my hand where the black tattoo marks were. "I can really see them going away while I'm doing this," Sharon said. Then I got to relax for a few minutes while she changed to the smaller laser. After the first treatment breaks up the pigment this laser breaks it up into even smaller particles. She began with a faster rhythmic TICK, TICK, TICK, TICK. It was not as severe — more of a burn than a stabbing plunge — and as it moved around my face, lips, neck and hands I kept thinking, This is double duty, John, it will go away twice as fast, just hold on, it will be over soon. Finally we were finished and Sharon asked how I was doing.

"It wasn't so bad," I told her it. "I had a special place I went for pain and placed myself there until the treatment was done." Sharon walked me to the reception area where Anita was waiting. We drove home as before, with me holding ice on my face to keep down the swelling. When Anita asked about the treatment I told her about the two different lasers. "It really wasn't too bad," I assured her. "The end justifies the means, Anita. Just remember that."

The swelling was more severe afterwards. I had to treat my face with hot compresses for two days to reduce the swelling.

While I was getting over the facial treatment my friend Ken called to check on me. He and Rhonda wanted Anita and me to go with them to visit Rhonda's folks in Shuswap Lake, British Columbia. I couldn't work in the woods because of fire danger and I wasn't due for another treatment until later that month, so a trip sounded like fun. It would be good to see Rhonda's parents again, and I had never been in Canada when I could see. It would be a first.

We would fly from Medford to Bellingham, Washington, where we would rent a car and drive through Vancouver and up through the Coast Range into British Columbia, spending our first night at Whistler. The next day we would make our way to Lac Le Jeune in British Columbia and an old fishing resort on a lake outside Camloops, then on to Shuswap Lake to Ron and Diane's house for a visit and more fishing.

I had always heard about the fishing in British Columbia, and I couldn't possibly say no. Ken and Rhonda had been so interested in my eyesight and my facial surgeries, and they had taken Anita and me places I had only dreamed about. I am truly blessed by these friends.

At this point some of the friends from when I was blind were kind of slow to come around. Perhaps they didn't know how to take me now that I could see, or maybe they didn't know what to say in this new situation. I knew I would love to see them all, but I had chosen to see Ken and Rhonda first, as I guess I felt to closest to them.

The arrangements were made and the four of us met and made our way to the airport for the flight to Bellingham and the six-day tour with Rhonda pointing out the sights of her home country and province.

It was slightly overcast when we arrived in Bellingham, which made it easier for me to see. After a short drive we crossed the Canadian border, where we stopped and exchanged money. We reached Vancouver during rush-hour traffic that was frustratingly slow, but I assured Ken the slow pace gave me time to see it all. Soon we were on our way to Whistler Mountain and our stop for the night. As we drove up the coast the road turned inland and the coastal mountains came into full view. The thing first I noticed was the trees growing out of crevices in the rocks. I started to point this out and

Rhonda said she could not believe it. She had lived there all her life and had never noticed that before. “Look up on the side of the mountain,” I said. “Wherever there’s a gap there’s a tree.”

Moving up the Coast Range Mountains we arrived at Whistler, the most beautiful ski resort I have ever seen. We had dinner in the hotel overlooking a ski lift that was still operating in July, with people skiing on the glaciers left from last season.

The next morning we drove the loop through the mountains to Lac Le Jeune, a spectacular drive through virgin land. Even the electric power lines had to be installed with helicopters, I was told. It brought back memories of Grants Pass when I was a child, before the forest was harvested. On the other side of the mountains we dropped down into plains that reminded me of going from the Cascade Mountains into Eastern Oregon. I had brought new telescoping spinning rods for Ken and me, and we hoped to get in some evening fishing at the lake. As we made our way across the prairie the wind began to blow, and we arrived in Lac Le Jeune to a fisherman’s worst nightmare. There was about a forty mile per hour wind blowing right down the middle of the lake, canceling our plans for fishing. Ken and I spent the next few hours watching the wind blowing whitecaps on the lake and bending the trees at an angle.

“Well, maybe it will blow out tonight,” Ken said. A true fisherman, he wouldn’t give up till the last light was gone. Finally as the light began to dim we realized there would be no fishing that day. We had a wonderful dinner at the lodge, and the next morning the lake was calm. We were waiting by the door of the boat rental and tackle shop when it opened, and got our boat and headed for the top of the lake. The storm had put the fish in deep water, so after a couple of hours we decided to move on to Rhonda’s parents’ home at Shuswap Lake.

Ron and Diane’s house was right on the lake, a gorgeous place, and they had planned a huge barbecue and party to welcome us as their American friends and to celebrate the thirtieth anniversary of their boat, the “Royal Baby.” It had been the pride of the lake in its day, and Rhonda had grown up using that boat.

Early Saturday afternoon Ken looked at me. “I don’t know about you, but I want to go fishing.” That sounded good to me, so

Ken went to find someone to take us out. Rhonda's sister April and her intended husband Ian were medical technicians in Vancouver and had come home for the party. I discovered that I had a lot in common with Ian. He had been a medic in the Canadian Army and I told him what it had been like to be a medic in the U.S. Army during the Vietnam War. Ian and April had brought their boat for the weekend, but Ian had to return to Vancouver for work, leaving April to take us fishing.

Now we had a boat and an operator. With its depth finders and monitors it was the most elaborate fishing boat I had ever been on in my life. It had all the latest gear, so we knew if a fish moved we would find it. Ken figured we needed a Canadian fisherman to get the right rigging so he asked Rhonda's Uncle Glen to come with us. As the four of us set out on the lake Ken began to ask Glen where we would get fish. Not to put any pressure on, Ken said, but we would hate to go back to the U.S. and tell everyone how bad the fishing is in British Columbia. Despite Glen's assurances we trolled around for a good two or three hours without a bite. We were getting blips on the depth finder indicating that the fish were twenty to fifty feet down. We raised and lowered the rigs and went right through the fish but there were no takers so we headed home.

We made plans to golf on Sunday and then try the fishing at Harper Lake on Monday. Rhonda suggested a nearby golf course overlooking the lake, so the next morning the six of us set out for the golf course.

The course was laid out so you hit off a vista over a valley onto a hill on the other side and then up to the green. I had never played a course like this before. Ken looked at me and said, "Well John, you've been playing — show us how." I took the ball out of my pocket and teed up and got my club, being careful not to move my head as I took my shot. It sailed about 200 yards and veered slightly to the left and landed on the hill on the other side. I had not hit the trees. Then it was Ken's turn, and Anita's and Rhonda's. Everyone played well, and I had one of my better days of golf. I didn't know if I was better on sloped courses or if I was simply having a good day. Whatever it was I was enjoying the game and the conversation as we made our way around the course. We returned home and sat outside that evening and watched the sun go down over Shuswap Lake.

The next morning we were to meet Glen for a day of fishing at Harper Lake. He had a boat on top of his truck and another in tow.

"Ken, you go with my son and I will take John and we will get some fishing in," Glen said. "I hope this will not take more than a couple of hours. We are allowed two fish apiece and I don't think that will be a problem."

The drive through the woods brought back memories from my childhood. The trees around the lake reminded me of Oregon. We followed the dirt road to the lake, where there was a dirt ramp to launch the boats. We unloaded the boats and put them into the water, then set up the motors and loaded our fishing tackle. As we pushed the boats out and started out onto the lake we could hear the calls of the beautiful loons of Canada.

As the electric motor purred Glen and I enjoyed hours of good conversation. Glen was close to my age and also had children. He could not imagine what it was like to never see his children, and then suddenly become able to see them. Glen got a fish and I had one bite but it got away. The others had caught three fish, and by then it was time to leave. Glen was disappointed, and said that the fishing was better a couple of weeks ago. But I'd had a wonderful day, and I assured him the fishing was good in Canada — it was the catching that wasn't so good.

We had to leave early the next day to catch our return flight in Bellingham. As I reflected over the past six days I realized that no one had stared at me like they had in the past. I was not ogled and gawked at, and no one had made a comment or stared at me. My face was getting well. I was to have a facial treatment the following day. The area around my eyes would be done with both lasers, and I felt a little apprehensive.

The next morning Dr. Naversen reviewed the results from the last treatment. The work with two lasers had removed a lot of scarring from my lower face and he was eager to see the results around my eyes and the upper portion of my face.

He put the numbing drops in my eye and inserted the eye shield, then gave Sharon instructions for applying the laser. Much like the previous treatment she started on my forehead, then down my nose and across my cheeks. This time I was ready. I had taken better precautions and not used all the energy that it takes to get to the place I have for pain. As I began to bear down she continued, but this time there wasn't the fiery stab, just the slow burn like a red-hot pellet rolling across my face. It moved over my forehead, along my eyebrows then down on each eyelid and below my eyes where the stain was really persistent, then to the left eye and the same procedure on the other side of my face.

When Sharon asked how I was doing I told her it was like before. It is really demanding and taxes me deeply. She said she could tell that it has to be painful. Dr. Naversen came in to remove the eye shield and asked how it was. I told him it was tolerable but it really taxed me, right to the end of my limits. He patted me on the shoulder and carefully plucked the shield from my eye and irrigated it so my vision would return to clarity.

I made my way to the car, applying ice packs during the ride home. This was the seventh treatment, including five around my eyes. After arriving home I treated myself with the hot compresses and after a day or two I began to resume life — mowing the lawn, smelling the fresh-cut grass, and golfing with Anita. The next thing on our calendar was a Lions event, a custom car show in Grants Pass at the end of July.

Chapter 14

Becoming a 'Regular Guy'

Anita had become a member of the Lions, too, and we had volunteered to help with the food booth, our big fund-raising event at the classic car show. I had volunteered to bring in the grill to cook the breakfast and hamburgers, so at four-thirty on the morning of July 29 I woke Anita. We had to be at Grants Pass City Park at six to help set up for the breakfast at seven-thirty. Our trucks were ushered in and I jumped out and helped unload the trucks in front of ours and soon we were unloading the grill and gas cylinders. There were a lot of Lions volunteers on hand, and by six-thirty people were arriving. It was to be a big event, with three or four hundred cars on display.

As the smell of bacon, ham and potatoes filled the air I looked up to see a procession of cars — '57 Chevys, some hemi-head Plymouths, Corvettes. This looked like Saturday night where I had just been, only that was thirty-two years ago. This stirred confusing emotions in me. I was in the present, and yet I was looking at the past. I felt a stronger kinship with the past than I did with the present. It's hard to explain, but what I was seeing was thirty-two years old, and I was twenty years old, not fifty-two. These were things that I had seen less than a year ago, only that year had been when I could see, thirty-two years ago. It's difficult to comprehend, this feeling of going back in time, but there was literally a space in my life that was gone. As I tried to absorb what was happening to me I was called back to the present. Breakfast was being served, the money was coming in, and everyone had big smiles on their faces. We hoped to make a lot of money at this event to pay for eyeglasses and hearing aids.

Anita was scheduled to cook hamburgers from ten to three, and I would come back and help take down the booth when the event was over. Meanwhile, Anita and I went to Heidi's house to watch Shelby and take her to the car show.

When we returned to the park with Shelby there were hundreds of old cars — '32 Deuces with big engines, all the hot rods from my era in the '60s. I looked around and saw people my age that I felt no kinship with, and people my children's age that I felt a great kinship with. I walked down the aisles of cars and explained to my granddaughter what they were and what model they were. She was excited, running from one car to the next just slightly ahead of me. This had been my first touch of the past, and I realized just what I had missed in life. My God, all those years as a young man and I was stuck in the past. All I could think was I wanted my life back. But I knew this was like catching a handful of wind. It was gone, and gone forever.

It took a few days to get over the shock I had felt at the car show. I finally talked with Anita about it, and she said she could relate to what I was feeling. We had looked desperately for a '68 Chevelle 396 Super Sport, the first car we had owned, and there wasn't one in the show. She admitted that she been swept away to the '60s and early '70s seeing all the old cars, and she thought that was why people our age had these old cars — to remember their young lives. All I could think was, You're right, Anita, and there are thirty-two years that I can't account for.

My facial treatments continued, and each one meant so much to me. When I looked in the mirror I could see the discoloration going away. Much like the cloak of blindness had been lifted from me, the aura of this awful facial deformity was being removed from my skin.

At my next eye appointment the technician took the pressure and then made another topography map of my eye. Reading the eye chart always gave me pleasure. I knew there wasn't any regression and maybe it would be a little better. Then Dr. Cherne came in and I told him about playing golf in Canada and how well I had done.

"When I look at your topography map I can see why. The surface of your cornea has really improved. It looks like a target — the circles are very round, like a rock that has been thrown into a pool. That is exactly what we want. I think we're on the right road and I think we need to do something about getting you some glasses." He examined my eye and when he came to my graft he said it was crystal clear. As always, it was music to my ears. The next good news was that I would get a prescription for glasses. I told Dr. Cherne that I had wanted to rip that eyeglass machine off the wall and take it with me so I could look through this huge device the rest of my life.

He laughed. "You won't have to go that far." I then told him about the old car show I had been to and how it had impacted my life and how I felt I could be stuck in the past. I had actually done more time than Rip Van Wrinkle by almost half again. When I looked back to the past I had a closer relationship to things that had gone by than things that were happening now.

"I could see how that could happen," Dr. Cherne said. "I truthfully see how that could be. With all you have been through things could be very confusing." Then he sat forward in his chair and explained that he would give me a prescription for glasses, that he might have to make an adjustment at my next appointment in two and a half months, but first I should find out how much I could see with this prescription.

I was elated. I had a prescription for glasses to correct my vision, and we hoped that when I put these spectacles on I would be able to see what I had seen through the machine all these months. When we got home I made an appointment immediately and ordered the new glasses.

The next thing on the calendar was an appointment to have a prosthetic eye made. Then yet another trip to Eugene to see Dr. You, this time to get an evaluation of my retina. My life at this time had taken a huge turn. My vision was so much better, and my face was getting well. I was becoming more outgoing, and things didn't bother me anymore. I seemed to be just one in the crowd. I was just like everyone else.

You wouldn't think that blinking could wear out a prosthetic eye, but there are actually grooves that are formed from blinking. Each one lasts about two to three years, so Rena Hoefling, the technician at the Veterans Hospital in Portland, usually makes two of the same kind. This time, I wanted a better match. Now that I could see, I explained, I looked at my artificial eye and I didn't really care for what I saw. I didn't want a white eye; I wanted one that was stained to match my other eye. The eye I was wearing was an old, worn-out prosthetic eye from the early 1980s. I had been wearing it because it was a closer match than the others.

Rena had me stand in front of a mirror and studied my eye. "I think I know what you want, John." We went into her office and she reached out and removed my artificial eye. Then she took the wax out of my eye to begin to make my new eye, making the shape very carefully to form the impression for the new one. She would try it and I would look in the mirror. "You're getting close, Rena," and after about four or five hours she had the perfect shape and the perfect fit. To me, it was a work of art. Now she would make this into plastic and it would be painted and have an iris attached so it would look like a natural eye.

Anita and I had lunch and then returned for the fitting. Rena took out the plastic eye that she had molded from the last impression. It was alabaster white, with an iris that was the same size and color of my real eye. She placed the eye in the socket and I looked in the mirror. At first I thought the bottom needed to be shaped a little more so my bottom eyelid would come up, but Rena explained that an artificial eye is heavier than a real eye, and after thirty-two years it had stretched my lower eyelid. She suggested waiting until my facial treatments were finished, and then a small surgical lid tuck might be needed to correct the problem. Rena took the eye out and moved to her workstation. She began to grind it down, but this last try to make it thinner was too much. She had ground a hole through the delicate new eye. I asked if it could be fixed.

"No, John, it would take me longer to fix it than to cast a new one. So why don't you and Anita go to dinner and come back in the morning at eight-thirty. I'll have a new one and we'll be where we are right now."

"I'm sorry that I'm being such a problem to you," I said.

"It's not a problem. I am very glad to do it for you — I just got a little over-zealous with the grinder."

The next morning Rena had the new eye ready. It was a perfect fit and a perfect match with my other eye, so all that remained was the final touch-up of veins and coloring. She did a wonderful job, and while we waited for her to apply the clear plastic coating Anita and I went to take care of paperwork. Although I carried my purple VA card showing that I was fully disabled and entitled to services, I was told my card was an "antique" and spent an hour and a half getting a new card. I now have six. This one is kind of nice, with an American flag, my picture and the words "service connected." I just hope this one works.

After lunch we returned to Rena's office for the final fitting. I was ecstatic — you could not tell my real eye from the artificial one. Another feeling came over me that this was part of the healing process of the past year. Both Anita and Rena assured me there was just enough twinkle in my new eye. I hugged Rena and thanked her for the special care that she had taken making this eye, and told her I would come back in two years for another one.

As Anita and I set out for the trip home I was beginning to think I lived at the wrong end of the state. It was 263 miles to Portland and 151 miles to Dr. Cherne's office in Eugene. We were really grinding up the highway.

While I had been in Portland my fellow Lions had been serving up hamburgers, French fries, ice cream, sodas and milk shakes at our largest fund-raising event of the year, the five-day Josephine County Fair. For the next three days Anita and I would take our turns in the food booth with our fellow Lions, working the two to seven-thirty shift. Anita grew up in her parents' small restaurant so she was well versed in running a kitchen and making hamburgers and sandwiches. My job was to be the ice cream man, making milk shakes and sundaes and filling in where needed.

I awoke Thursday morning full of enthusiasm, as I knew the money we made would be well spent. Anita and I put on our Lions shirts that say Grants Pass Lions Club with our logo, a caveman riding on a lion's back. I also sported a Lions hat.

We arrived at the fairgrounds a little early so we could learn our jobs. Anita went to the front of the concession booth and I went to the side window where one of my fellow Lions showed me where the ice cream bars were and explained how to make the milk shakes and how to serve sodas and dishes of ice cream. He showed me the supplies and how to refill the ice cream machine. It would be my job, in between customers, to make sure the front was stocked with salt, pepper, ketchup, and other things. Before starting my shift I went up to check on Anita and found her up to her elbows in tomatoes, onion, lettuce and condiments, making hamburgers as fast as she could.

"Are you having fun?"

"You bet," she said, "but I'm not used to this and three days will really be a job."

"It's a labor of love, Anita."

"I know it," she said. I returned to my area just as Jim was finishing his shift and cleaning up. I told him I was ready but I wanted to go over it one more time to make sure I didn't miss anything. He showed me again and then said I had it. I thanked him and felt very comfortable. For the next three days I would be the head soda jerk on the middle shift.

I had served two or three sodas and several dishes of ice cream when I got my first order for four milk shakes. The customers watched as I put the ice cream and flavoring into the twenty-ounce cups and then added milk to the proper level. I placed the first one back under the ice cream machine to fill it before putting it on the milk shake mixer. The first one went fine. I picked up the second one, and when I pulled the lever on the ice cream machine it came off in my hand. The ice cream kept pouring out, and I didn't know what to do. All I could think was, This must be what Tim Conway looked like in some of his comedy shows. As I kept trying to push the handle back into the hole the glass was getting fuller and fuller. Soon it was overflowing and the ice cream was running down my hand. People began to chuckle and I thought, My gosh, I've got to figure out what to do. Suddenly it came to me. I held the handle up to my eye and saw threads on it. I placed it in the hole and after two or three turns it stayed in place. I pushed the handle up and the flow of ice cream stopped.

There was a huge glob of ice cream on the floor, and my hands were full and the cup was filled to the brim. I set it aside and made a replacement milk shake and filled the orders. Things went well after the handle was tightened, and I placed the milk shakes on the counter and took the money, acting like nothing was wrong. People were still smiling as they walked away, and I didn't see how they could stop laughing at me. It was so funny that I was laughing at myself. One of the other Lions working in the food booth heard me laughing and came back to see what had happened. He began to laugh as I cleaned the ice cream off the floor, then it was all over the food booth and everyone was laughing. When I was blind things like this had happened to me all the time, but I could tell it was going to happen even now that I could see.

My life was so wonderful now. I always tried to be upbeat on life and laugh at things, and it did make it easier. For the next three days I worked alongside my fellow Lions. We made nearly $10,000 dollars for eyeglasses and hearing aids for needy people in our home county. The most amazing thing that happened at the fair was that as I served people not one person stared at my face — not a single one. I blended in like any other fifty-two-year-old soda jerk at the Lions food booth at the Josephine County Fair.

It was time for my one-year retina check-up. I didn't expect a problem as my vision was continuing to improve and I was eager to get my glasses in a few days. Anita and I drove to Eugene the next day with time for lunch and window-shopping in the mall before my appointment with Dr. You. I enjoyed these walks with Anita, holding her hand and pointing out things I saw in the windows. It was an activity I had missed for thirty-one years. We would go to the mall and walk, but it was always Anita explaining things to me. Now I could see for myself this wonderful world we live in.

Soon it was time for my eye appointment. As we entered the office I was shown to the back where the technician placed drops in my eye and took the pressure. It was in the normal range at twelve. Then she asked me to read the eye chart. The lights were dimmed and there was my old buddy, the big E, then the H and the B on the 20/100 line. I read the 20/80 line, but I couldn't go any farther. She handed me the paddle and I could read all the lines down, including the 20/40 line.

"John, your vision is staying good. We are so happy for you." I told her it seemed to get a little clearer every time. Since Dr. Cherne took the stitches out my distance vision was getting clearer. Things are a little fuzzy up close but I have glasses on order and this should change, I explained. "I may need another lens or another prescription later but I am going to be able to see what I can see using the prescription machine."

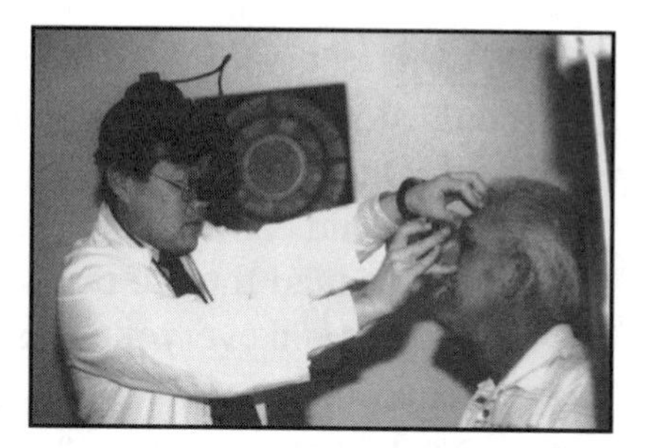

Dr. Timothy You declares my retina "rock solid." Another worry eases as I marvel at the miracle of sight.

She left for a moment and returned with Dr. You.

"You're seeing 20/40 John, isn't that unbelievable?" Yes, I told him, and I had glasses on order.

"Do you realize with this 20/40 vision you will be able to do some limited driving?" I was taken aback. I never thought that would be possible.

"I have the vision to see but I am not ready to drive because my reaction time is too slow," I explained.

"Not now," Dr. You said. "When the time comes and you are ready, you ask us and we will see what we can do." Then he moved the slit lamp into position and began his examination. Again my graft was crystal clear.

"John, I can't believe what I am looking at. Your eye is doing so well." Then he got the big lens to check my retina and held it in front of my eye and looked at the back of my eye as I looked up, down, and to each side. "John," he said as he turned his light off, "it is rock solid. It has not moved one bit. I really want you to know the worry is over now. For the first year your retina can move if it is going to. I don't think we will have a problem with it but I want to keep an eye on it. I want you to see me every six months like we have talked about in the past, for the rest of your life. We will keep a close eye on your retina." Then he sat down in his chair and asked what I had been doing. I explained how my eye had improved after Dr. Cherne removed the stitches and how I had been playing golf and volunteering with the Lions, and how rewarding it was to participate in their activities.

"I know," Dr. You said. "I joined the Lions myself." We said good-bye and I thanked this talented young man one more time for what he had done to restore my retina so I could have this wonderful vision and enjoy my life.

I was happy and somewhat relieved to find out that the chances of my retina detaching were slim. This was one more thing that was fitting into place with my rehabilitation. Everything was coming together, I reflected as I lay in bed that evening. The next morning I would get my new glasses, and there were a million thoughts running through my mind, of what the world would look like when I could see it even better. I drifted off to sleep with dreams of the future and a clearer view of my wife's face and my daughter's face and my granddaughter's face and yes, even a better look at my own face in the mirror when I shave each day.

The next morning I awoke at four-thirty, eager to be there when the optometry clinic opened. Anita teased me as I prodded her to hurry, and I told her I was like a big kid — I really wanted to get my glasses.

We were there when the door opened, and when I sat down the young lady said, "I bet I know what you're here for." I had a big smile on my face as I replied, "Yes, I have been waiting thirty-two years for this, so can we please hurry?" She laughed and went to get my glasses ready. When I put them on it was like magic. Instantly her face got three times clearer, as did her beautiful blonde hair and blue eyes and her lab coat. I turned to look at my wife. I could see Anita clearly and I knew this was the biggest development thus far. When I turned my head it seemed like I was standing still and everything else was moving fast, much like when I got my sight back for the first time. This was not a concern to me. I knew I could adjust. The technician took the glasses off to adjust one earpiece, then asked how they felt. They were very comfortable, and the plastic lens made them a lot lighter than I had expected.

As I turned around to look at the eye chart there were huge tears welling up in my eye. This was the best I had ever seen, even through a machine. She asked me to read the smallest line I could see, but I couldn't. I was trying to blink back the tears, but finally they ran down my cheek and I wiped them off. I began to blink frantically as I started at the top of the chart. I could see the E and the H and the B, then I began to read the lines one after another. I read the 20/40 line and then I went to the 20/30 line and I could read it, too. This was more than I could have imagined would be possible. It had only been 360 days exactly from my corneal transplant, from first being able to see a light shined in my eye to being able to read a 20/30 line on an eye chart. It was overwhelming to me. The young lady also had a huge smile on her face. "You did real well, John."

Our next stop was Wal-Mart, where I would have my first clear look at my daughter Heidi. As Anita drove I thought of each and every one of the past 360 days, turning them over in my mind like pages in a calendar. I thought of all the major events in my life in such a short period of time. The operation that restored my sight. The facial treatments that were now at the halfway point. The ability to be just a regular individual and blend into a crowd, not sticking out like a circus sideshow. The relationships with my children and my lovely wife. I knew all this had been given to me by God. I didn't know why but I had been chosen and I felt truly blessed. I didn't know what was in store for me for the rest of my life, but I knew God would give me the strength to never give up.

For the first few days after I received my glasses everything was wonderful. Things were much like I remembered them as a twenty-year-old man in the service. Then things seemed to blur just a bit and my eyes became ultra-sensitive to the summer sunlight. The self-adjusting glasses didn't darken enough, so I ordered a pair of clip-on sunglasses to fit over my glasses.

When I went to pick them up the following week I once again turned around to read the eye chart. This time I could only read to the 20/40 line. Things had blurred just a little, but Dr. Cherne said it would do that. On the way home I told Anita I was amazed that my vision had dropped that much in only a week. She reminded me of what Dr. Cherne had said, but still, it seemed to change more than I expected.

Over the next few weeks my vision began to worsen. I kept telling myself that it would change, but somehow my inner thoughts wouldn't let me accept that. I kept wondering, Is this the beginning of the end? Could this be the rejection that Dr. Cherne had warned me about? Anita said I was foolish, but I didn't think so. I had received so much bad news in my life that I feared even this wonderful blessing could be taken away. I called on my old buddy George Foreman to give me strength to get through this process but somehow he lacked the ability to give me inner peace this time. I began to wake up at night, terror-stricken, and even though I could still see my clock it was blurrier. My eyesight would get better for a day or two, then worsen again. By my birthday on October fourth I could barely read the cards from my children. With two weeks to go before my visit with Dr. Cherne, I was extremely scared. Everything since my operation had been a step forward. This was a reversal and I was having a terrible time with it and with the fear of going back to that darkness I lived in for thirty years, eleven months and seven days.

I was deeply concerned as I marked off each day on the calendar until my appointment with Dr. Cherne. As we drove to Eugene I could still see the same things from the car window, but they were blurry. I wiped my glasses constantly, thinking they were dirty.

At the clinic my worst fears were confirmed. I could only read the eye chart to 20/70 with my glasses. Then I was given the paddle and I could read the eye chart to the 20/40 line and some of the 20/30 letters. It was a great relief, as it told me my eyes could be corrected again. Then a topography was taken of my eye and I was ushered back in to wait for Dr. Cherne. He came in, looked at my chart and asked how I was doing.

"Quite frankly, Doctor, I am not doing very well. I don't see as well as I could when I got my glasses." He looked at the topography map.

"No doubt your eye has changed. Try taking your glasses off and read. You probably see better without them than with them."

"You have to be kidding me," I said. "I never tried that." He laughed. "Yes, it has changed a lot. I knew it would. You had been so anxious to see I could not hold you back anymore so I gave you a prescription. I'll give you another one today and it will bring your vision back." Then he looked at the topographical map and had me look in the eyeglass machine again. Just a few flips of the lens and I was right back where I was before. Then he had me place my face in the slit lamp to examine my eye. He and turned on the light and said "Your cornea is so clear, I just cannot believe how clear it is. It is ultra clear." With that statement he put all my fears to rest. The regression in my vision had been temporary. It was only a matter of new glasses. I had tormented myself needlessly over the fear of rejection of my cornea. But to be honest, I don't know if I will ever get over that fear. It is overwhelming to think I could go back to where I was for thirty-one years and lose the wonderful life that I have now.

I was continuing the twice-monthly treatments on my face, with number thirteen coming up to work around the eye area. The tattooing below my eyes was being kind of stubborn but we were well over halfway to where I would not have any of the discoloration on my face. At this point I could blend into a crowd, and no one ogled me or stared at me anymore. It is so good to be just another guy. Not a blind guy bumping into things or a tattooed face that someone makes a comment about. Just a normal human being. Dr. Scott Cherne and Dr. Timothy You gave me my life back, and

Dr. Douglas Naversen was allowing me to live it. These wonderful men practice medicine for the sake of medicine, not to become multimillionaires. Dr. Cherne and Dr. You accepted Medicare payments to restore my eyesight. My cost was a $100 co-payment. Dr. Naversen has accepted what Veterans Affairs will pay, leaving me with no medical bills. My life was snatched away from me before it really got started, but I choose not to think of what might have been but rather to look at the way Anita and our family made the best of a horrible situation. I put my faith and trust in my family and I have been justly rewarded. Anita and I share a love that most people only attempt to have. The relationship I have with my children is extraordinary. As I enter the final third of my life I find myself truly blessed. I know how things will be for the rest of my life, and I will savor it for what it is. If something bad happens I only think of the good that happened that day. I don't have bad days now. I simply can't, because I am the luckiest man in the world.

I am truly blessed. After a corneal transplant restored my vision, facial treatments restored my appearance and allowed me to live my life fully.

Afterword

In closing, I would like to share some thoughts with you, the reader. First, my story and the events described in this book are absolutely true as I recall them. In addition, one of the things that I have noticed since regaining my sight is how little we care for one another. I have found it very rewarding to be a member of Lions International, as they care about people and are working to put an end to blindness. Nothing is easy for a blind person — absolutely nothing, from achieving basic sanitation while traveling to simply getting dressed in the morning. The Lions, in their volunteer activities, are dedicated to putting an end to these difficulties for people all over the world. If you really want to feel good about yourself by helping others I encourage you to consider becoming a Lion. You will be greatly rewarded for your efforts.

I have also learned that it is good to be a little nosy about the health conditions of your friends and loved ones, and to make sure they receive proper treatment. If it hadn't have been for my cousin Don Williams in Coos Bay, Oregon, I would have been disfigured and blind for the rest of my life. There was no help from Veterans Affairs or other government agencies. Somehow or other I seem to fit at the bottom of somebody's budget in the federal government. Things were promised but never provided. All I got was Don't worry, buddy, and We will take care of you, and You are a top priority, and You will receive the finest health care for your service … but somehow this never materialized.

When I was a young man and needed help in rehabilitation it was much easier for someone to tell me to sell cigarettes and magazines in a federal building instead of spending a little money and giving me an education I could have used for the rest of my life. I had to call on my congressional representatives to help me get what was due me, constantly working through the bureaucracy to prove my eligibility to receive benefits. The medical cards that are issued, one after another, and the clerks and patients' account coordinators that make decisions in the government have to be a huge financial drain on the system. Dollar for dollar, I would like to know how much goes to veterans instead of administration.

How many hundreds of thousands of dollars do you think it took to restore my life? To restore my eyesight and to make my face normal and acceptable after my injury in the service? Do you think it would cost a couple hundred thousand dollars to restore my eyesight? How about $150,000? No, less than that. Maybe $50,000? No, less than that. The actual cost for the surgery that restored my eyesight was $5,557.88. That is the entire amount that the government paid, and I have the payment receipts in my possession. Oh, there was more billed, you can believe it, but the doctors and hospital accepted assignment. The total cost for my pre-op visits, hospitalization, surgery, and one year of follow-up treatment from Dr. Cherne and Dr. You was $5,557.88, and my cornea was a gift from the Lions Eye Bank of Oregon. Wouldn't it be a shame if the decision was made not to spend that money by some clerk at the VA and I had to be blind that extra thirteen years? Before I went through this ordeal that thought would have never entered my mind. But I have related what I went through to get approval for the treatment of my face and how the battle was finally won. And Dr. Douglas Naversen has agreed to take payment from the VA pay schedule of $595 per visit to restore my face to its normal condition. This is going to cost slightly more than restoring my eyesight, but it has given me the ability to live a normal life. When everything is finished the restoration of my life will have cost the government about $25,000, or well under $30,000 if it takes a few extra visits. For most people that is less than the cost of an automobile. I would like to think that my situation was an isolated incident, but I can't quite believe that. How many other veterans are in the system, defeated by the bureaucracy and resigned to a poor quality of life that could be fixed? I know I am not alone.

I prayed for God to reach someone's heart to approve paying for this procedure and my prayer was answered, like many other prayers. A wonderful woman who worked in the Roseburg office read Dr. Naversen's letter and saw the photos of my face. She was deeply touched and she championed my cause and pushed my claim through for approval. The staff at Dr. Naversen's office informed me that this lady had kept track of my treatment and remained interested in me. She knows who she is and I know who she is, but most importantly God knows who she is.

My hope is that some good can come of this. It's late now and I would like to end this book like I end every day and will continue to do so for the remainder of my life. I walk over as Anita makes her way down the hall and just before I turn the light off I take one last look at the two of us in the wedding photo that my daughters gave me on our thirty-second anniversary. I look at these two young people, so full of hope for the future. Then I look at Anita and see the results of the faith that we have in one another and I thank God for another wonderful day.

After I prepare for bed and kiss Anita good night and as I wait for sleep to come I ask God to hold the spirit of my donor very tenderly. Then I ask God to bless the International Lions for the work they do in helping the blind. I pray for continued health of Dr. Scott Cherne and Dr. Timothy You, and to bless the staff of the Clear Vision Institute. Then I pray for the health of Dr. Douglas Naversen to continue his fight against facial deformities, and to bless the staff at Laser Associates. Last, I ask God to give my fellow disabled veterans and the blind people of the world the strength to endure one more day and to give them the strength to NEVER GIVE UP.

Order Form

Never Give Up: A Veteran's Journey to Sight and Healing
ISBN 0-9741654-0-9

Quantity	Price per copy	Total price
	$14.95	$
	Shipping	$
	Total	$

Name ______________________

Address ______________________

City ______________ State ______ ZIP ______

Telephone ______________________

(Daytime phone, if we have questions about your order)

Check enclosed in the amount of: $______________

Make check payable to: John C. Malkow
Mail to: John C. Malkow
P.O. Box 740, Murphy, OR 97533

Price: $14.95 U.S., $21.95 Canada
Shipping: $3.95; for orders of more than 1 copy add $2.00 per additional copy
Quantity orders: For shipping price for 10 or more copies call: 541.862.2858

Thank you for your order. Please allow 7-10 days for delivery.

A portion of the sale of each book will be donated to the Oregon Lions Sight and Hearing Foundation.